Technology
for Motor Mechanics

PART 4

Technology for Motor Mechanics

PART 4

S. C. Mudd, T.Eng. (C.E.I.), F.I.M.I., A.M.B.I.M., M.A.E.T.

Deputy Head, Department of
Technician and Motor Vehicle
Engineering
Huddersfield Technical College

Edward Arnold

© S. C. Mudd 1971

First published 1971
by Edward Arnold (Publishers) Ltd.,
41 Bedford Square
London WC1B 3DP

Reprinted 1973, 1975, 1978

ISBN: 0 7131 3252 3

Printed in Great Britain by
Fletcher & Son Ltd, Norwich

Preface

This book has been written to help the motor mechanic in the final stages of his apprenticeship. The material provided meets the syllabus requirements of the City and Guilds of London Institute, and the Regional Examining Boards, for the Third and final years of the Light and Heavy Vehicle Mechanics' courses, and of the Technician Course in the Technology subject. It should also be of help in the Workshop and Related Studies subjects of these courses, and in the course for the compression-ignition engine mechanics' certificate.

It is hoped that this book, together with his further education, practical experience and training, will enable the apprentice to understand the basic principles of the more complicated and precision-built units and systems incorporated in the modern vehicle. This understanding should then enable him to derive the maximum benefit from the more detailed courses provided by the various manufacturers, and perhaps help him to choose a specialization later on in his career.

In view of the heavy syllabus loading in these years of the course it is also hoped that teachers may find the book suitable for class use, and that its use in this way may make more time available for the real work of teaching and learning.

Huddersfield
1971

S. C. MUDD

Acknowledgements

The author wishes to express his grateful thanks for the advice and active assistance so generously given by his colleagues, and by the following companies:

A.C.–Delco Division of General Motors Ltd.
Armstrong Patents Ltd.
The British Leyland Motor Corporation Ltd.
Borg & Beck Ltd. (One of the Automotive Products Group)
Bosch Ltd.
C.A.V. Ltd.
Crypton Equipment Ltd.
The Dunlop Rubber Co. Ltd.
The Ford Motor Co. Ltd.
Girling Ltd. (Sales and Service)
Hardy Spicer Ltd.
Hepworth & Grandage Ltd.
Hobourn–Eaton Manufacturing Co. Ltd.
Joseph Lucas (Sales and Service) Ltd.
The Lockheed Hydraulic Brake Co. Ltd. (One of the Automotive Products Group)
Metalastik Ltd.
Perkins Engines Ltd.
Rolls Royce Ltd. Motor Car Division
Rootes Group School
Smiths Instruments
Westinghouse Brake and Signal Co. Ltd.

Contents

1 The Compression-ignition Engine

In general construction and arrangement the four-stroke diesel or C.I. (compression-ignition) engine is very similar to the four-stroke, spark-ignition engine. Similar components are used in both types of engine, the particular operating requirements of each being met by relatively small but important variations in design. The essential difference between the two types of engine lies in the way in which combustion is started and controlled – all other differences following from this.

In the spark-ignition engine the compressed, heated, and turbulent *mixture* of air and vaporized petrol in the combustion chamber is.

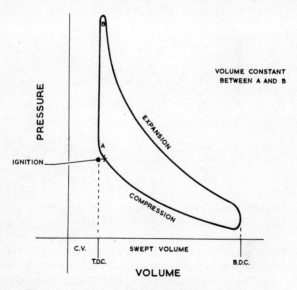

Fig. 1.1 Spark-ignition combustion (*constant volume*)

ignited by an electrical spark. The spark is a very small area of intense heat which then expands rapidly as the flame spreads throughout the mixture, the speed or rate at which it spreads, i.e. the rate of combustion, being uncontrollable.

In the C.I. engine *air only* is subjected to much greater compression and turbulence, and after compression the temperature of the air usually exceeds 1000 °C. This temperature is well above the self-ignition temperature (flash point) of fuel oil, so that when an atomized spray of fuel is forced into the very hot, dense, and turbulent air in the combustion chamber the burning starts spontaneously. The rate of combustion after ignition is controllable directly by the rate at which fuel oil is forced into the chamber, i.e. by how much fuel is injected. Note that the C.I. engine has no electrical ignition system and no carburettor. These are replaced by the fuel-injection system, which is very much more reliable.

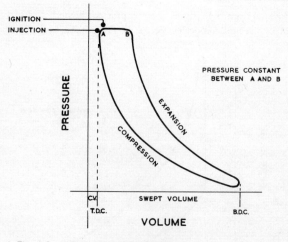

Fig. 1.2   Low-speed compression-ignition combustion
(*constant pressure*)

The compression ratios of spark-ignition engines have been increased in recent years in order to obtain greater thermal efficiencies and better fuel economy. The normal maximum, with readily available fuels, is about 10:1, this limitation being due to the fact that it is a mixture of air and petrol which is being compressed – and this mixture will detonate at the pressures produced by a compression ratio of about 10:1.

The compression ratios of C.I. engines range from about 14:1 up to about 22:1 but the majority of British engines have ratios of about 16:1. These high ratios are essential to the operation of the engine and their use is possible because air only – and not a mixture of air and fuel – is compressed.

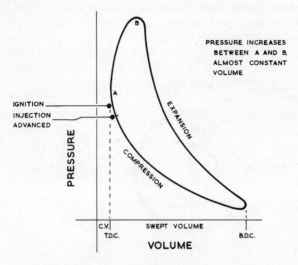

Fig. 1.3   High-speed compression-ignition combustion
(*semi-constant volume*)

These higher compression pressures result in higher maximum cylinder pressures during combustion. The components of the C.I. engine must therefore be stronger and heavier than those of a comparable spark-ignition engine and, in order to minimize the inertia stresses in the heavy rotating and reciprocating parts, the maximum speed of the engine must be limited by some form of governor. Due to its higher compression ratio, the C.I. engine has a higher thermal efficiency, this being about 35% as against the 20% to 25% of the spark-ignition type. The C.I. engine therefore has the better fuel consumption, usually consuming between a half and two-thirds of the fuel consumed by a spark-ignition engine doing the same work.

Although the maximum cylinder pressure is the higher in the C.I. engine its mean or average pressure is the lower, and this results in the spark-ignition engine having the greater power output and developing the greater torque.

FOUR-STROKE CYCLE

The valve timing of the C.I. engine is similar to that of the spark-ignition engine – valve lead, lag, and overlap being used to improve the volumetric efficiency (see Fig. 1.4).

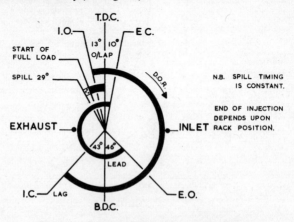

Fig. 1.4   Compression-ignition timing diagram

Induction
The inlet valve is opened before tdc, and the exhaust valve is closed after tdc as the piston moves down the cylinder to create a depression. The difference between this reduced pressure and the higher atmospheric pressure forces air only to pass through the air cleaner and the inlet manifold to charge the cylinder. The inlet valve is closed after the piston has passed bdc.

Compression
As the piston moves up the cylinder towards tdc the charge of air is compressed into about one-sixteenth of its original volume, the pressure rising to between 3100 kN/m^2 and 5100 kN/m^2 and the temperature

to about 800 °C. As compression ceases, i.e. just before tdc, fuel injection is begun and combustion is initiated.

Power

At the beginning of combustion the temperature of the gases may momentarily exceed 1600 °C, with a corresponding pressure in excess of 6900 kN/m². The pressure forces the piston down the cylinder to produce torque at the crankshaft, the pressure being sustained by the continued combustion of the fuel injected over a number of crankshaft degrees (see timing diagram and combustion phases). The exhaust valve is opened before bdc and the spent gases begin to leave the combustion chamber under their own pressure.

Exhaust

The piston passes over bdc and moves up the bore to complete the scavenging operation. The inlet valve is opened before tdc to commence the next cycle, the exhaust valve being closed after tdc.

COMBUSTION PROCESS

The combustion process of the C.I. engine can be considered to have three stages or phases (see Fig. 1.5).

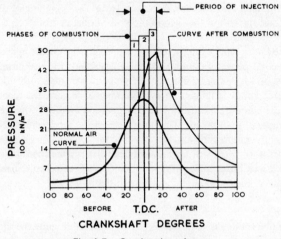

Fig. 1.5   Combustion phases

First phase or delay period

The fuel oil is sprayed into the dense and very hot air under a high pressure. The pressure forces the liquid fuel to break up into very small droplets which form a spray. In this state the fuel will not burn, and there is a small but measurable period after injection before ignition occurs and combustion is begun. In this period the droplets of fuel are heated and mixed with the air but only their surfaces are vaporized and therefore only this small amount of fuel releases heat energy. The temperature and pressure of the air is only slightly increased during this delay period – the period usually extending from about 10 to 5 crankshaft degrees before tdc.

Second phase

This follows on after the first phase and the two are very closely connected. In this phase all the fuel injected has had time to be mixed thoroughly with the air, and has absorbed sufficient heat for the droplets to be completely vaporized. The vapour is ignited and burns very rapidly, the temperature momentarily exceeding 1600 °C and the pressure 6900 kN/m². As the piston passes over tdc the pressure has fallen to about 5000 kN/m². The rate or speed at which the pressure rises in this phase determines the degree of combustion or diesel knock produced, the faster the rise the louder the knock.

The number of crankshaft degrees between the beginning of the first phase and the end of the second phase is almost constant. If, for any reason, the delay period is too long the second phase will be too short – and the knock will be intensified as the pressure rise occurs in less time. The second phase of combustion usually extends over 10 crankshaft degrees and is normally completed by about 5 degrees after tdc. The degree of knock is influenced by a number of factors, the main ones being the amount of air turbulence, the ignition quality of the fuel, and the temperature of the air. The turbulence of the air depends upon the speed of its compression and the shapes of the combustion chamber and the inlet port. Most C.I. engines knock at low engine speeds; at these speeds knock is due to the combination of lower temperatures, reduced turbulence, and the minutely small quantities of fuel being injected.

Third phase

In this phase there is sufficient heat to vaporize and ignite the fuel as it emerges from the nozzle. The rate of combustion is now controlled directly by the rate of injection, i.e. the quantity of fuel sprayed into the chamber. Injection ceases at a variable point after tdc but the burning continues as the piston moves down the cylinder. The piston is therefore subjected to *sustained* high pressures which produce a more even torque at the crankshaft than is possible with the spark-ignition engine.

FUEL PROPERTIES

C.I. engine fuels, like petrols, are hydrocarbons. Their flash points are much higher than petrols, so the fire risk associated with their use and storage is much less than with petrol. The fuel used in C.I. engines for road vehicles consists of about 87% carbon, 11% hydrogen, 1% oxygen, and 1% sulphur. The sulphur content must be kept as low as possible to reduce the possible formation of corrosive sulphuric acid during combustion.

The most important property of C.I. fuel is its ability to self-ignite – with the shortest possible delay period of combustion – when sprayed into the dense and heated air in the combustion chamber. This ability affects the rate of pressure rise in the second phase and therefore the intensity of combustion knock.

Cetane number

C.I. engine fuels are rated by their cetane number. This is the percentage by volume of cetane ($C_{16}H_{34}$) in a test mixture, composed of cetane and alpha-methyl-napthaline ($C_{11}H_{10}$), which has the same self-ignition qualities as the fuel being checked.

The ignition quality is found by running a test engine under specified conditions and finding the length of the delay period, in crankshaft degrees, by the use of an engine indicator. The fuels with the shorter delay periods are the better fuels. These will produce the least combustion knock and provide the easiest starting from cold and the smoothest running. Good-quality fuels will have cetane ratings of 60 or over, while the poorer fuels will rate down to about 30 cetane.

Additives

Additives such as amyl nitrite and ethyl nitrate will increase the cetane rating of a fuel by reducing the delay period of combustion. They will also reduce the ignition temperature and the maximum combustion pressure. These advantages could be gained by the use of less than 5% by volume but C.I. fuel additives do not work in all circumstances. They also increase the fire risk, and are expensive, so they are not widely used commercially.

In the spark-ignition engine the fuel is well mixed with the air before it enters the combustion chamber. In the C.I. engine the fuel must be kept apart from the air until the moment of injection. They are then required to mix thoroughly, ignite, and burn – all at the same instant. This cannot be arranged to perfection but the action can be made to occur fast enough for practical purposes; the main reason for the special shape of the combustion chambers of C.I. engines is to achieve this.

As the C.I. engine depends upon the heat produced by the compression of the air to ignite the fuel, the combustion chamber must have a low surface-to-volume ratio so that heat losses are kept to a minimum.

If the quickest possible mixing of the air and fuel is to be obtained the air must be made to move violently and break up the fuel spray. The violent air movement is called turbulence and is the combination of swirl, in which the air moves through a path similar in shape to a helical spring, and squish, in which the air is squeezed from the cylinder into the combustion chamber near the end of the compression stroke. Swirl is imparted to the air on the induction stroke by the shape and position of the ports. It may be increased by the use of integral masks on the inlet valve, the mask giving the air a spiral movement. Masked valves are prevented from rotating by the use of a special type of valve spring retainer. The degree of turbulence varies between different designs of combustion chamber but it is always greater in C.I. engines.

There are two main types of chamber used in C.I. engines and these are known by their position relative to the cylinder. Those in which the chamber is formed in the piston crown are called 'direct-injection' types. Those in which the chamber is completely in the cylinder head, or mainly in the head and partly in the piston, are called 'indirect or separate-chamber types. Most British engines are of the direct-injection type but the Perkins is a popular engine which has separate chamber-injection.

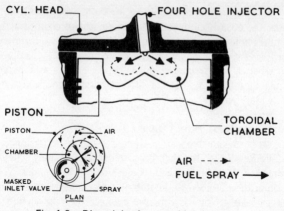

Fig. 1.6   Direct injection – swirl turbulence

Direct injection (Figures 1.6 and 1.7)

These chambers often have masked inlet valves to promote extra swirl, and squish is produced at the end of compression. Due to the low surface-to-volume ratio, heat losses during compression are slight, so heater plugs are not needed for cold starting. Also due to the low heat losses, direct-injection engines generally have a higher thermal efficiency and a lower fuel consumption than separate-chamber types. They have a higher mean pressure, and combustion knock occurs more frequently and is more pronounced. As the chambers are larger, higher injection pressures must be used to ensure the correct reach of

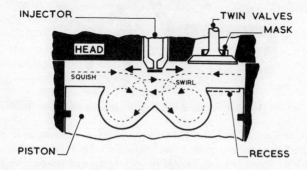

Fig. 1.7   Direct injection – Saurer dual turbulence

spray. Injection pumps and injectors are therefore subjected to greater stresses and absorb more power. Direct-injection chambers are fitted with multi-hole injectors – usually four-hole nozzles are employed but more holes are used in some designs. Generally, direct-injection engines have a better torque curve, i.e. flatter over the speed range, than separate-chamber types but the latter develop more speed and consequently more power.

Separate chamber (Figures 1.8 and 1.9)
These are also known as air-cell and precombustion-chamber types. In the Perkins design the chamber is very approximately spherical and is formed in the cylinder head to one side of the cylinder. The outer portion of the chamber can be unbolted when decarbonizing becomes necessary. Air is forced from the cylinder into the chamber via a tapered, tangential entry which helps to provide a more thorough mixing of the air and fuel. The larger engines are fitted with a two-hole nozzle while the smaller have a single-hole nozzle of the pintle type (see nozzle types).

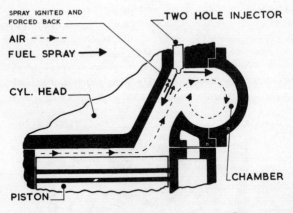

Fig. 1.8   Indirect injection – Perkins aeroflow

In the Ricardo designs the chamber is closer to the cylinder and the piston has a specially shaped recess near the entry to the chamber. A two-hole nozzle is fitted. Heater plugs are required for cold starting but in the smaller engines, where adequate cylinder head cooling may be more difficult to obtain, the Pintaux nozzle is used. This special type of nozzle will provide easy cold starting without the use of heater plugs or air-intake heaters.

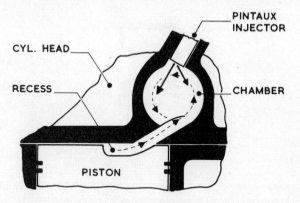

Fig. 1.9   Indirect injection – Ricardo type

Some separate-chamber designs incorporate a device by means of which the compression ratio can be increased to obtain more heat when starting from cold. This is usually a screwed plug which is moved into the chamber when starting and unscrewed once the engine is running. Some Lister engines have a starting compression ratio of 19:1 and a running compression ratio of 15:1.

ENGINE COMPONENTS

As the maximum cylinder pressures are higher in the C.I. engine than in the spark-ignition engine, each engine component has to be made stronger, and will therefore be larger and heavier. The pressures are also more sustained, so bearing surfaces must be larger and of tougher material. The materials used are white metal and copper–lead, lead–bronze and aluminium–tin alloys. White metal beds in well and has a high resistance to attack by acids but will not resist high pressures unless used in the form of thin-wall bearings. The bronzes will resist high pressures and bed to the shaft reasonably well but are vulnerable to acid attack and must be used with a hardened journal. Aluminium–tin alloy is now superior to these other bearing materials and does not require the hardening of the journals. Phosphor–bronze is used for gudgeon-pin bushes.

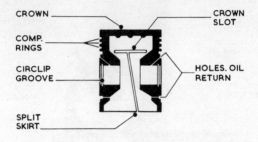

Fig. 1.10   Piston of spark-ignition engine

Like the pistons of spark-ignition engines (Fig. 1.10), the pistons of the C.I. engine (Fig. 1.12) are made from an aluminium alloy which is tough and fairly hard wearing. As they have to operate under higher and more sustained pressures they have to be longer and heavier in proportion. The crown is thicker and the gudgeon-pin bosses are more heavily reinforced. In direct-injection types the crown will include the combustion chamber and the valve clearance recesses. It may also incorporate a heat-barrier slot to control the heat flow in the piston. Three or four compression rings are usually fitted, together with two oil-control rings. Split-skirt pistons are not normally used. Groove

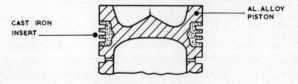

Fig. 1.11   Ring insert

wear may be minimized by the use of cast-iron groove inserts (Fig. 1.11) which are installed when the piston is first produced.

The piston rings follow normal practice but special types may be used in two-stroke engines in order to maintain adequate sealing when the

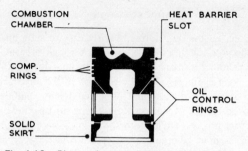

Fig. 1.12   Piston of compression-ignition engine

aluminium-alloy piston is cold. Taper section rings may be used to reduce ring 'stick' while the 'fire' ring provides better cold sealing and also reduces the operating temperature of the piston (Fig. 1.13). In

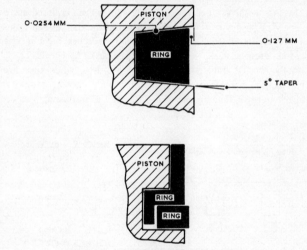

Fig. 1.13   Taper ring (*top*) and fire ring

the Rootes opposed-piston engine, the body of the piston is made of cast iron, while the crown is made from a heat-resistant steel. The crown is heat insulated from the body by air gaps and this feature, together with the absence of a cylinder head, results in very small heat losses and a corresponding high thermal efficiency. Easy cold starting is normal and a 12-V electrical system is adequate.

COLD STARTING

Direct injection engines are normally fairly easy to start under cold conditions because the amount of heat lost through the walls of the combustion chamber is small. This is due to the low surface-to-volume ratio of the open chambers. The compression of the air charge must always be carried out quickly and under cold-start conditions this necessitates the use of 24-V electrical systems to operate the more powerful starter motors. These motors, due to the very high compression ratios used, must be pre-engaged types in which the drive pinion is engaged with the flywheel before it is rotated. The engagement may be obtained manually or by the use of a solenoid. It is, of course, most important that the state of charge of the batteries be maintained at a high level.

Some engines are fitted with decompression devices which are used to hold the engine valves open until the engine has been cranked up to starting speed. The device is then released to allow the sudden compression of the air charges. A few stationary engines have inertia starters which are essentially separate and very heavy flywheels. These are manually rotated until a high speed is reached, when they are suddenly engaged with the crankshaft through a special coupling. Their stored energy is then absorbed in rotating the crankshaft.

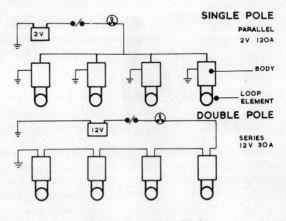

Fig. 1.14　Heater plug circuits

Engines employing separate-chamber injection are generally more difficult to start from cold as their heat losses are greater. This difficulty may be overcome by the use of battery-powered heater plugs (see Fig. 1.14), one of which is fitted into each combustion chamber. These supply sufficient heat in a few seconds to vaporize the fuel and start combustion. Some engines are fitted with an electrically powered heater coil, arranged in the intake manifold, which heats the air on its way to the combustion chambers by igniting a fuel spray delivered by a hand pump.

The CAV Thermostart (Fig. 1.15) is a small device which is screwed into the manifold and supplies both heated air and vaporized fuel as the engine is cranked. It consists of a small, tubular body, the central passage being sealed by a ball held to a seat by stem. The passage is filled by fuel which is gravity fed from a tank of 2500 mm³ capacity, the tank being replenished automatically by a small feed from the main filter. The body is surrounded by an electrically heated coil which has an extension. The extension acts as a fuel igniter, and the whole assembly is surrounded by a tubular, perforated shield.

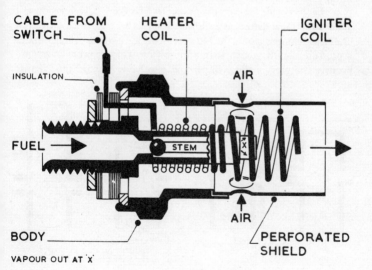

Fig. 1.15   CAV Thermostart

When the engine is cold the ball valve is closed. When a battery current is passed through the coils the heat produced causes (a) the body to expand and open the valve and (b) the fuel passing through the valve to vaporize. The vaporized fuel is then ignited by the heat of the igniter coil and heats the air passing through the manifold. When the current is switched off the flow of air cools the body and the valve is closed as it contracts.

Another aid to easier cold starting is the use of ether. This very volatile and inflammable liquid is sprayed into the intake manifold as the engine is cranked – the small amount of heat available being sufficient to cause the ether vapour to first self-ignite and to then ignite the fuel being injected. Great care must always be taken in the storage, use, and disposal of the aerosol type of spray canisters used.

TWO-STROKE C.I. ENGINES

A serious disadvantage of the two-stroke, spark-ignition engine is that it has a low thermal efficiency. This is due to (a) the incomplete scavenging of the exhaust gases and (b) unburnt mixture passing out of the combustion chamber with the exhaust gases. Two-stroke C.I. engines do not suffer from these defects as a blower or supercharger is used instead of crankcase compression – the blower forcing air into the cylinder under a pressure slightly greater than atmospheric. This air provides a more positive charging of the cylinder and also helps to expel the exhaust

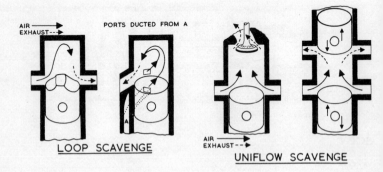

Fig. 1.16   Scavenge systems

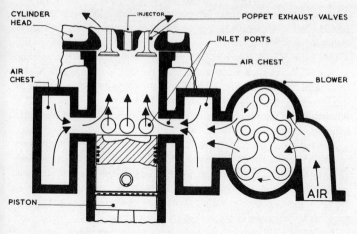

Fig. 1.17   Two-stroke compression-ignition engine (valved)

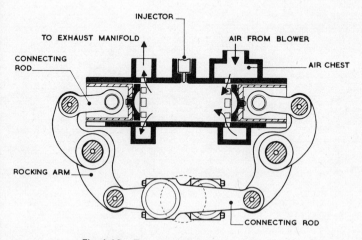

Fig. 1.18   Two-stroke engine (ported)

gases without wasting fuel. The two-stroke advantage of an increased number of power strokes per crankshaft revolution is, of course, retained.

One type of two-stroke C.I. engine has twin, poppet-type, exhaust valves which are rocker operated, while the inlet ports are arranged in the cylinder walls (see Fig. 1.17). These ports communicate with an air box or chest, which is kept charged with air under pressure, and the movements of the piston control the flow of air from the chest into the cylinder.

A very successful two-stroke C.I. engine is the opposed-piston type in which two pistons are arranged in one long and open-ended cylinder (Fig. 1.18). The inlet ports are controlled by one piston and the exhaust ports by the opposing piston. The combustion chamber is formed between the two heat-resisting crowns of the pistons as they come together at the centre of the cylinder.

Two-stroke C.I. engines have higher fuel consumptions than four-stroke types due to their lower volumetric efficiency, less complete combustion, and less positive scavenging of their exhaust gases. They have the advantage of a better power-to-weight ratio and are usually more compact. Cylinder wear is usually the greater in two-stroke types, the Rootes opposed-piston type being a notable exception.

2 The Fuel-injection System

SYSTEM (Figure 2.1)

In the C.I. engine a special type of plunger pump and an injector are used to introduce fuel oil into the hot, dense, and turbulent charge of air in the combustion chamber. One pump and one injector are used for each combustion chamber but the separate pumps are grouped into a common body, and all are driven from the one camshaft arranged in the lower part of the body.

The pumps generate pressures of between $10\,350\,kN/m^2$ and $20\,700\,kN/m^2$. The pressure required to atomize the liquid fuel, and to force it to penetrate the dense air charge, varies between engines and depends upon the compression ratio and the type of combustion chamber – direct-injection chambers needing the higher pressures. The injection pressure is determined by the spring loading upon the needle valve in the injector.

As the pumps and injectors have to operate under these very high

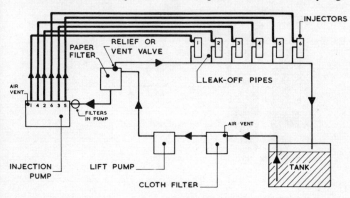

Fig. 2.1   Compression-ignition fuel system

pressures, the clearances between their moving parts have to be very small indeed. It is of vital importance that all traces of dirt and water be removed from the fuel in order to protect these units from rapid wear and destruction. The fuel system of the vehicle, and the storage arrangements for bulk fuel, must be designed and used in such a way that dirt and water are rigorously excluded.

On the vehicle the fuel is carried in one or more tanks mounted at the side or rear of the vehicle. The tank has internal baffles to prevent the surging of the fuel from damaging the tank, and it may be arranged

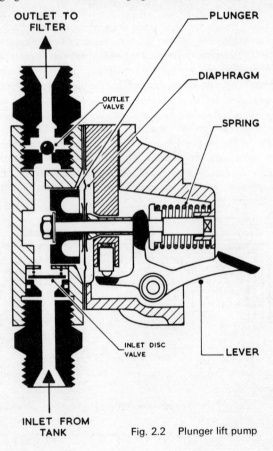

Fig. 2.2   Plunger lift pump

on rubber pads. It must be vented to the atmosphere, and the drain plug may carry a wire-gauze filter which surrounds the lower end of the intake pipe to the lift pump. In many systems a cloth-element filter is fitted between the tank and the lift pump. The lift pump may be a single- or double-diaphragm type similar to that used in petrol supply systems but the diaphragms are resistant to fuel oil. Diaphragm types are used in low-pressure systems and deliver at about $34.5 \, kN/m^2$. Some systems require higher delivery pressures and in these plunger pumps are used, the plunger being backed up by a diaphragm to prevent fuel seepage. These pumps deliver at about $104 \, kN/m^2$. (See Fig. 2.2.)

The lift pumps may be driven from the camshaft of the engine or from the camshaft of the injection pump. They deliver fuel to one or two filters of the paper-element type which are usually arranged above the level of the injection pump. These filters can extract extremely small particles of dirt and the elements are replaced at regular intervals. The cloth elements in the preliminary filters can be washed a few times in clean petrol before they need replacing. These filters (Fig. 2.3) are

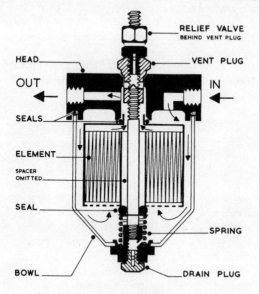

Fig. 2.3   Compression-ignition fuel filter

fitted with drain plugs and air vents, and the paper types have pressure relief valves which permit excess fuel to return to the tank when the lift pump delivers at a rate greater than is being injected.

The fuel passes from the paper filter into the main gallery of the injection pump. In the more modern pumps it is again filtered by small replaceable elements built into the pump. From the gallery the fuel passes into the barrels of the pumps and is measured or metered out into the quantities appropriate to the speed and load of the engine, and is also placed under a high pressure. Fuel under high pressure is trapped between the pump and the injector at all times, and when the pump pressure exceeds the trapped pressure the injector valve is opened and the fuel is sprayed into the combustion chamber. Some fuel always escapes around the injector needle and is not injected. This 'leak-off' fuel is collected from the injectors and is returned to either the tank or the intake side of the preliminary filter. Note that this quantity of fuel must be taken into account when fuel consumption tests are carried out.

The pipes connecting each pump to its injector are made of steel and must have cold-upset or welded nipples. Their characteristic is wall thickness to enable them to resist the very high pressures – a typical pipe being about 8 mm outside diameter with a bore of 2 mm. Ideally they should all be of the same length so that distortion, due to the pressure impulses, affects them all equally. The low-pressure piping varies in size from about 10 mm to 15 mm outside diameter, with a wall thickness of about 1 mm. Bends should not be of less than 50 mm radius and all piping must be well supported.

THE INJECTION PUMP

Function

The injection pump has to:

(a) Build up a pressure sufficient to atomize the liquid fuel, and to force it the required distance through the dense air charge.

(b) Meter out the quantities of fuel very accurately, and vary these quantities to suit the weight of air induced at every combination of engine speed and load.

(c) Deliver the correct quantities of fuel to the injectors at the correct moment relative to the position of the pistons, in the correct firing order, and at equal angles of crankshaft rotation.

Construction

The injection pump is mounted on, and driven by, the engine. It is driven at such a speed, and is so timed to the engine, that the full expansion of the charges of air coincide with the pistons being in the best position to exert the maximum force on their crankpins. High-speed C.I. engines may have automatic devices which advance the beginning of injection as engine speed is increased.

The pump consists of an aluminium-alloy body which houses the separate pumps, their operating and control mechanisms, and the governor. The pumps are supplied with fuel from a common gallery, and each is operated by its own cam on the single camshaft driven by the engine. The cams are radially disposed around the shaft in firing order. All the pumps are controlled from the same rack gear connected to the governor.

Each pump in the assembly is called a pumping element and each element consists of a very accurately machined plunger and barrel (see Fig. 2.4). These are supplied as mated pairs and must always be

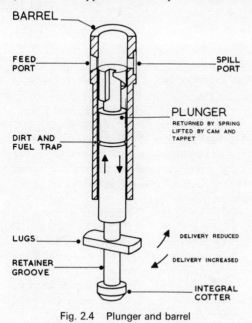

Fig. 2.4   Plunger and barrel

kept together. The barrel has two ports at its upper end which communicate with the gallery (Fig. 2.5). The top of the barrel is sealed off by a spring-loaded delivery valve of special shape.

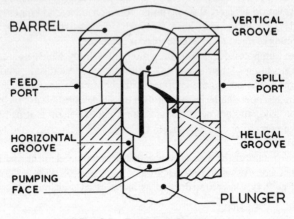

Fig. 2.5   Two-port element

The plunger is grooved both horizontally and vertically, and also has a helical groove or helix which begins near the upper end of the vertical groove and ends directly opposite at the upper edge of the horizontal groove. The lower face of the horizontal groove is the sealing or pumping face, and all the space between this face and the delivery valve must be filled by fuel at all times. If air should enter the pump it must be expelled by bleeding or venting. The lower end of the plunger is grooved to fit a spring retainer and this end also has two lugs which engage with slots machined in the lower end of a cylindrical sleeve. The sleeve fits around the lower part of the barrel and carries a gear quadrant which is meshed with the rack. The quadrant is clamped to the sleeve in such a way that the movement of the rack results in the sleeve, and the plunger, turning in relation to the barrel. The plunger is forced down by the action of its spring and up by the action of the cam. A roller tappet is interposed between the cam and the plunger, and the clearance between the two is adjustable. The movement of the rack is controlled by the governor and not directly by the accelerator pedal. Figure 2.6 shows the element assembly of the injection pump.

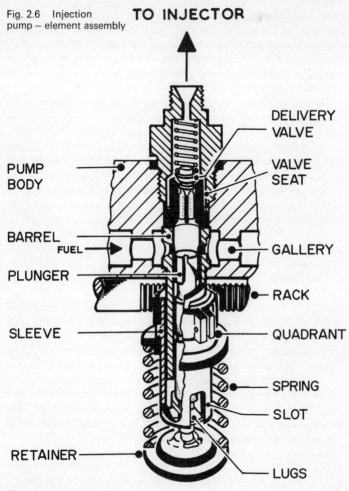

Fig. 2.6 Injection pump — element assembly

TO INJECTOR

DELIVERY VALVE

PUMP BODY

VALVE SEAT

BARREL

FUEL

GALLERY

PLUNGER

RACK

SLEEVE

QUADRANT

SPRING

SLOT

RETAINER

LUGS

Element operation

The delivery valve is closed down to its seat, trapping fuel between it and the injector needle valve seat. This fuel is under a pressure just below that required to lift open the needle valve.

The barrel is full of fuel and as the cam and tappet lift the plunger fuel is displaced back to the gallery via the ports. Further lifting results in the ports being closed by the plunger sides – and as the fuel is totally enclosed the pressure is increased. When this pressure exceeds that trapped in the pipe line and the injector, the pressure difference opens the delivery valve and the higher pressure acts at once on the needle valve of the injector – forcing it to lift from its seat and allow fuel to enter the combustion chamber.

The spraying action continues until the lifting of the plunger results in the helical groove uncovering its port (spill port). At this instant the fuel is no longer enclosed and spills back into the gallery. The pressure in the element collapses at once, and reduces the pressure in the pipe and in the injector. The injector needle at once returns to its seat and spraying or injection ceases. The delivery valve is similarly returned to its seat by its spring, the two closing actions taking place so quickly that a high pressure is retained in the injector and pipe line. This enables the next delivery to operate without having first to build up pressure at the injector. Note that the injector delivers the same *quantity* of fuel as the plunger forces through the delivery valve – but not the same portion of fuel.

The quantity of fuel delivered by the element is varied, as the plunger moves up and down, by the action of the rack and sleeve. Rack movement turns the quadrant and sleeve, the sleeve turning the plunger via the slots and lugs. As the plunger is turned the helical groove uncovers the spill port at different plunger-lifting positions – so releasing the pressure sooner or later. Turning the sleeve and plunger clockwise increases the quantity of fuel delivered and vice versa. When the vertical groove is aligned with the spill port there can be no delivery at all, i.e. cut-off is obtained. The gear quadrants are adjustable in their position on their sleeves and they must all be set so that all elements make the same delivery at the same speed. This adjustment is known as 'calibrating', i.e. checking *size* of delivery.

The points at which the deliveries are made must occur at equal angles of crankshaft rotation. These points are adjusted by varying the tappet clearances. The maximum delivery per plunger stroke varies with engine capacity but is usually less than $10 \, \text{mm}^3$.

In a different type of element (Fig. 2.7) the barrel has only one port and the upper end of the plunger has one helical groove machined in its side. This groove communicates, via a small hole, with a cylindrical hole in the centre of the plunger head. The metering control operates in the same manner as the two-port element. The rack and quadrant may be replaced by a rod-and-fork mechanism but the principle of turning the element to vary the quantity of fuel delivered still applies.

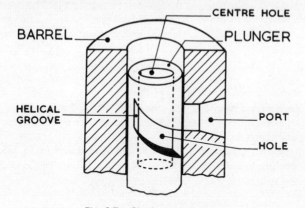

Fig. 2.7   Single-port element

These pumps are all constant-stroke types, i.e. the plunger always lifts the same amount but the delivery is variable. They are also known as 'jerk' pumps.

THE DELIVERY VALVE

Function
The delivery valve acts as (a) a non-return valve between the injector and the pumping element and (b) an injector anti-dribble device.

Construction
The valve and its seat are arranged in the injection pump body immediately above the barrel of the element, the lower face of the seat acting as the end of the barrel. The valve is spring loaded such that it always tries to close down to its seat, the sealing faces being bevelled (Fig. 2.8). Below the bevelled face is a plain cylindrical portion, the volume of which is so proportioned as to produce the correct drop in pressure as the valve closes. This plain portion is of the same diameter as the grooved guide portion below it, and both fit into an accurate bore in the valve seat. Pressure generated in the pumping element acts upon the lower face of the plain portion via the grooves in the guide.

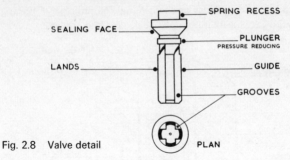

Fig. 2.8   Valve detail

Operation (Figures 2.9 and 2.10)
Start of delivery. There must be a high standing pressure in the injector and pipe line to ensure an immediate start of injection. As the plunger

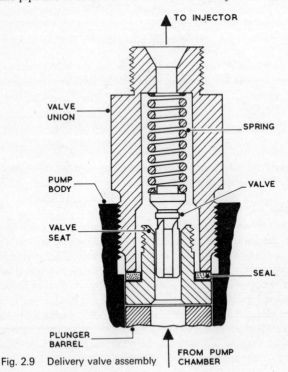

Fig. 2.9   Delivery valve assembly

is lifted it closes the ports in the barrel and the resulting pressure acts on the underside of the plain portion of the delivery valve. When this pressure exceeds that held in the pipe line the delivery valve is forced from its seat. The instant the lower face of the plain portion clears its bore the higher pressure is transmitted through the fuel to the needle valve of the injector. This valve is lifted against its spring pressure and fuel is sprayed into the combustion chamber, the spraying continuing until the helix of the plunger uncovers its port.

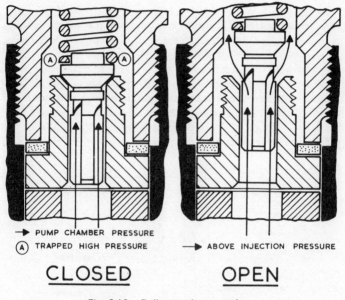

→ PUMP CHAMBER PRESSURE
Ⓐ TRAPPED HIGH PRESSURE   ➝ ABOVE INJECTION PRESSURE

CLOSED   OPEN

Fig. 2.10   Delivery valve operation

End of delivery. As the port is uncovered, the fuel is no longer enclosed and the pressure at once collapses. The delivery valve is at once returned to its seat by the action of its spring but in returning the plain portion, as it enters its bore, acts as a plunger pump – suddenly increasing the effective volume of the pipe and injector. This in turn results in a sudden pressure drop in the injector which enables its needle valve to close in one swift movement, i.e. without bounce and fuel dribble. The bevel face then contacts the seat and maintains a pressure in the pipe and injector which is just less than that required to lift the needle valve of the injector.

INJECTION PUMP TESTING

Two main tests and adjustments have to be carried out in the servicing of injection pumps. These are known as calibration and phasing.

Calibration
Function
This test or operation is carried out to ensure that all the separate pumping elements are delivering the same, correct quantity of fuel at each point over the speed of the engine. As each individual delivery or shot is so very small it is common practice to measure, in cubic centimetres, the total delivery made over 100 or 200 shots. This delivery must be made at specified rack-opened positions and at specified pump speeds. The test figures, and the limits allowed for differences from them, are supplied by the pump manufacturers and are different for different models and makes of pump.

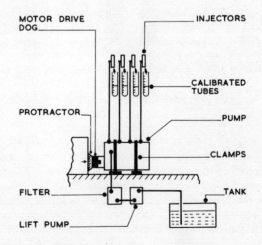

Fig. 2.11   Pump-testing machine

Machine (Figure 2.11)

The machines used in the testing and adjusting of injection pumps vary in design but usually incorporate the following features:

(a) Variable speeds of rotary drive.

(b) A revolution indicator or tachometer.

(c) A set of test injectors.

(d) A set of test tubes calibrated in cubic centimetres.

(e) A protractor scale, which can be moved, on the drive dog.

(f) A fuel tank and filter with either a gravity or pump feed to the injection pump.

Method

(a) Setting up. The inspection plate of the injection pump is removed to allow access to the plunger tappets and the sleeve-adjusting quadrants. Each element in turn is then checked to ensure that a clearance exists between the top of the plunger and the bottom of the delivery valve. This is done by turning the drive dog of the pump until the plunger is at the top of its stroke. It should then be possible to lift the tappet and the plunger very slightly by means of a screwdriver. In the CAV B-type pumps this lift should be 0·5 mm. This clearance may be made or adjusted by altering the tappet clearance by either the adjusting and locknuts, or by shims. The drive dog of the pump is then engaged with the drive dog of the machine and the pump clamped to the machine bedplate. Delivery pipes of equal length are connected between the injectors of the machine and the pumping elements. The fuel supply pipes are connected between the machine and the pump, and the pump is then run at 600 rev/min for a short time to expel all air from the system. The rack 'stop' position is then used to make certain that fuel is not delivered when the 'cut-off' control is operated.

(b) Calibrating. The rack is now set at exactly 12 mm open from the stop position and is locked. The pump is then driven at 600 rev/min and the deliveries over 200 shots are collected in the calibrated tubes below the injectors, one tube for each injector. The individual deliveries are then compared with each other and against that specified by the manufacturer of the pump. Any adjustments found necessary are made by repositioning the quadrant upon its sleeve in each case. These adjustments are a trial-and-error process and are continued until all of the elements deliver quantities within the limits specified by the pump manufacturer. Should an element prove incapable of being adjusted to

come within these limits, the plunger and barrel must be replaced by a new set. An erratic or varying delivery is usually an indication of a faulty delivery valve. This must be replaced. Similar tests are then made with the rack set and locked at 9 mm and 18 mm open. The test is then concluded with a series of checks at 200 rev/min; if these result in deliveries below those specified the cause is excessive wear and the barrels and plungers must be replaced. Note that adjustments are made only at the start of the series of checks. When all the elements are delivering fuel within the specified limits the sleeves and quadrants should be marked by a freshly scribed line. This makes easier any later adjustment or correction if the quadrant should move on the sleeve during service.

Phasing
Function
This operation is carried out to ensure that the pump makes its deliveries at equally spaced intervals of its camshaft rotation. The interval, or phase angle, will be 90° for a four-element pump and 60° for a six-element pump.

Method
This operation is usually carried out after calibration. The delivery pipes are removed from the pump, together with the delivery valve and spring of No. 1 element. A swan-necked pipe is connected into the delivery valve holder, and the pump rack is set and locked at 12 mm from the stop position. The drive from the machine is disconnected to enable the pump to be turned by hand.

The drive dog of the pump is slowly rotated by hand until fuel flows freely from the swan-necked pipe, being expelled by the plunger's upward movement. A point can then be reached where, by very slow and careful turning, the last drop of oil can be made to move in and out of the end of the pipe. This is the instant of spill cut-off, i.e. the instant when the plunger closes off the ports in the barrel as it is lifted by the tappet.

More accurate methods are now available in which the phasing is checked electronically, the first fuel particles to leave the injector operating an electronically controlled valve which results in the illumination of a revolving pointer. The pointer indicates the phase angle.

When the spill point is obtained, the protractor reading is noted, or the protractor scale may be moved around the drive dog and set to zero. The delivery valve and spring are replaced in No. 1 element and the operation is repeated for the other elements in firing order. The pro-tractor readings at the spill point of each are noted and the intervals are compared. The pump is considered to be correctly phased, and requires no adjustment, if the intervals are equal within the limit of 0·5°. If adjustments are necessary they are made by adjusting the tappet clearance until the phase angles are correct.

This same method of finding the spill cut-off is used when timing the pump to the engine, it being considered for this purpose that spill cut-off is the same point as the commencement of injection.

C.I. ENGINE GOVERNORS

Function

A characteristic of the C.I. engines used in road vehicles is the tendency to instability at idling speeds. This may be due to the difficulties of metering accurately the very minute quantities of fuel required at these speeds, combined with the effects of reduced air turbulence and slightly lower compression temperatures. The first function of the governor therefore is to automatically control fuel delivery to provide steady idling speeds.

The components of the C.I. engine have to withstand higher and more sustained pressures than those of the spark-ignition engine. These components must therefore be stronger and heavier. The very large stresses imposed upon them, due to their rapid changes in motion, will result in their eventual failure unless their speeds are limited. The second function of the governor is to limit the inertia stresses by limiting the maximum speed of the engine.

At speeds intermediate from idling to maximum the driver usually has direct control, the governor not overriding the pedal linkage at these speeds. This type of governor is known as the idling and maximum speed type, and is of mechanical construction, i.e. is operated by the effects of centrifugal forces upon rotating flyweights.

Pneumatic governors provide accurate control of engine speed at all points in the speed range and, due to their small weight and volume, are particularly suitable for the smaller engines.

Hydraulic governors are exceptionally reliable and are particularly suitable for use with two-stroke engines. They are much more expensive to produce and so are usually only used where smooth slow running is of importance, e.g. on long-distance coaches. These types also control at every point on the speed range.

Construction (Figure 2.12)

In these types two flyweights are arranged on pillars secured to a sleeve fitted to the end of the camshaft of the injection pump. The outward movement of each flyweight (due to centrifugal force as the sleeve rotates) is controlled by three springs, and is relayed to a crosshead via two bell crank levers. The movement of the crosshead is in turn transferred to the lower end of a floating lever which can pivot on an eccentric. The eccentric is integral with the pedal shaft and both the eccentric

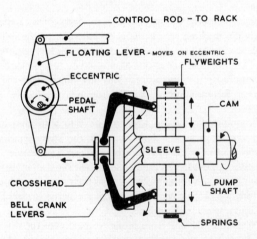

Fig. 2.12   Construction of mechanical governor (idling)

and the lever can be moved by the turning of the pedal shaft. The upper end of the floating lever is connected to the delivery-control rack of the pump via a manually operated stopping or fuel cut-off mechanism. This can be operated without affecting the operation of the governor in any way.

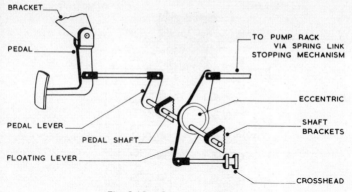

Fig. 2.13 Governor linkage

Operation (Figure 2.13)

Starting. The accelerator pedal is fully depressed, so turning the eccentric about the pedal shaft. As the crosshead is held by the bell crank levers the upper end of the floating lever is forced inward to move the rack to its maximum fuel-delivery position. The starter motor is then engaged and energized. When the engine starts and runs up to speed the pedal is released, and is returned to its stop by its return spring. The eccentric again pivots about the pedal shaft centre and at the same time the movement of the crosshead, due to the flyweights, causes the floating lever to move on the eccentric and pull the pump rack back to the minimum fuel position.

Idling. At idling speed only the outer springs of the flyweights (see Fig. 2.14) are opposing their outward movements. If the idling speed should fall below the pre-set speed the outer springs will force the flyweights inward. The crosshead will be moved and will move the floating lever on the eccentric to increase the volume of fuel delivered until the preset speed is obtained. If the idling speed should exceed the preset speed the flyweights will move outward against their outer springs. The crosshead will move the floating lever on the eccentric to reduce the volume of fuel delivered until the preset speed is obtained.

Intermediate speeds. These are controlled directly by the driver, the pedal shaft turning both the eccentric and the floating lever about the end of the crosshead, i.e. about the lower end of the lever. Irrespective of the position of the crosshead, the upper end of the lever is moved to

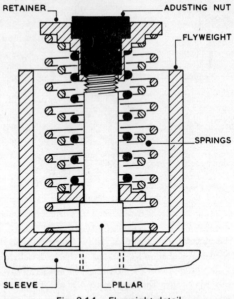

Fig. 2.14   Flyweight detail

increase or reduce the volume of fuel delivered as the driver wishes. At these intermediate speeds only the outer springs of the flyweights are compressed, the inner springs opposing further outward movement of the flyweights.

Maximum speed. If the pedal is depressed to give more fuel than is needed to overcome the load against which the engine is working, the

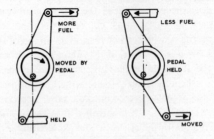

Fig. 2.15   Mechanical governor: intermediate (*left*)
and governing positions

engine speed will tend to exceed its pre-set and safe maximum value. The flyweights will move outward against their inner springs and the floating lever will be moved on the eccentric – so reducing the volume of fuel until the preset speed is obtained. The governor overrules the pedal in this event, and as the limited speed is reached the flyweights are moved inward to their correct position by their inner springs.

Stopping control

Manual. In this device a lever link is pivoted at the upper end of the floating lever. A link screw is threaded into the link at one end while the other end passes through two springs and a link block. The link block is attached to the end of the rack and can be contacted by a spring-loaded lever pawl. The pawl is secured to a cross shaft to which the control lever is clamped. When the lever is moved to the 'stop' position the pawl forces the link block to slide along the link screw – compressing the springs and pulling the rack into the zero delivery position. When the engine has stopped and the lever is released the springs return the rack to the maximum delivery position. Where a manual stopping control is employed, the control rod or rack has an adjustable stop arranged at the driving end of the pump. This consists of a sleeve which is screwed into the pump body and surrounds the end of the rack. The outward movement of the rack is limited by a stop which is screwed into the end of the sleeve and is locked by either a nut or a split pin.

Spring link. In some governors the spring-link part of the stopping control is preloaded. This improves the governing action at maximum speed and stops the excessive fuel delivery which is characteristic of mechanical governors. Where this type of 'idling speed', 'maximum speed', and 'stopping' control stop is employed, the usual maximum-speed stop at the end of the rack is replaced by an excess-fuel device. This is used to permit excessive fuel deliveries for cold starting, and consists of a small, spring-loaded plunger which is arranged at $90°$ to a small cylindrical bore in the end of the rack. The plunger carries an adjustable stop with a cylindrical end which is slightly less in diameter than the bore in the rack. In the normal maximum fuel-delivery position the outward movement of the rack is limited by its end contacting the stop. When excess fuel is required the plunger is forced inward to allow the rack to move farther – its bore enclosing the end of the stop. As the engine starts and the rack moves back, the plunger is returned to its normal position by its spring.

The engine is usually stopped by lifting the accelerator pedal back beyond its normal idling position, the pawl forcing the plunger back and moving the floating link in such a way that it pulls the rack into the zero delivery position.

THE PNEUMATIC GOVERNOR

This type of governor provides accurate control throughout the speed range of the engine. It consists of two units connected by a flexible pipe. The venturi unit is arranged between the intake manifold and the air cleaner, and the diaphragm unit is built into the end of the injection pump.

The venturi unit consists of a throttle valve and a venturi. In practice the venturi is not as shown in the diagram (Fig. 2.16) but is much

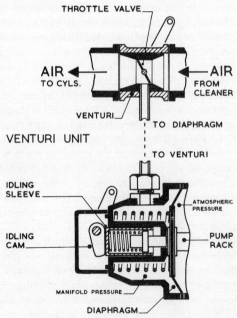

Fig. 2.16   Pneumatic governor

smaller and is arranged at one side of the main air entry. The throttle valve has adjustable maximum and minimum speed stops.

The diagram unit consists of a small chamber which is sealed by a leather diaphragm. The diaphragm is secured to the end of the pump rack and is spring loaded in such a way that the rack is normally being forced towards the maximum delivery position. The spring side of the diaphragm is subjected to the varying degrees of depression produced in the venturi unit by the passage of air to the cylinders. The opposite side of the diaphragm is subjected to atmospheric pressure at all times. The pressure in the venturi depends upon the air velocity, which in turn depends upon the quantity of air entering the engine. This type of governor therefore makes the injection pump directly sensitive to the weight of air entering the engine.

Operation
Starting. The accelerator pedal is fully depressed, opening the throttle or air valve. The governor spring forces the rack into the maximum fuel-delivery position. When the starter motor is engaged and energized air is induced into the engine which then starts and runs up to speed.

Idling. When the engine has started, the pedal is released and its spring brings the air valve back to its idling stop, severely restricting the flow of air. A large depression is therefore produced in the manifold and this is communicated to the chamber of the diaphragm unit. The diaphragm has a large pressure difference between its two sides which causes it to move against the action of its spring – so pulling the rack back into the minimum fuel-delivery position. This reduces the power of the engine and its speed is reduced to that set for idling conditions.

Accelerating. As the pedal is progressively depressed, the air valve is opened – so reducing the depression in the venturi, and the pressure difference between the two sides of the diaphragm. This allows the diaphragm spring to move the rack progressively nearer to the maximum fuel-delivery position – so increasing the power and speed of the engine until the air valve is held against its maximum speed stop.

Maximum speed. If the engine should tend to exceed its preset maximum speed with the air valve fully open the increased supply of air will produce its own depression (due to the size of the venturi). This will result in the diaphragm being moved to reduce the fuel supply and so bring the engine back to its normal maximum speed.

An auxiliary spring is used to help stiffen the diaphragm at idling speeds only and is brought into action by a special shape of cam. This prevents any violent movements of the rack following fluctuations of air pressure.

The maximum fuel delivery is limited by rack stops of the sleeve type, and an excess-fuel device and a cut-off control are provided.

Some pneumatic governors have two small venturi connections, the second being connected to an air valve fitted in place of the idling cam and spring. At idling speeds below those set, the diaphragm opens this valve to admit atmospheric pressure into the chamber. This reduces the pressure differences and therefore results in the engine speed being increased to the preset value. At speeds above idling, the valve communicates depression in the same way as the other pipe.

THE HYDRAULIC GOVERNOR

This is an all-speed governor in which the rack position is determined, throughout the speed range of the engine, by the action of the governor and not directly by the pedal. The hydraulic governor has the advantage of eliminating the high stresses and torsional vibrations associated with the use of mechanical governors on engines with a wide range of speeds. It is very accurate and is particularly suited to two-stroke engines, but it is more expensive than other governors.

Construction (Figure 2.17)

The governor is built into the end of the in-line injection pump and the interior of the governor is filled with fuel from the gallery of the pump.

The main components of the governor are a gear-type pump driven by the camshaft of the injection pump, an amplifying piston, an amplifying valve, and a spring-loaded servo piston. The servo piston is linked to the rack of the injection pump, and its spring side is subjected to rack-closing fuel pressure. The opposite side of the piston is subjected to rack-opening pressure, and the pressure difference across the servo piston causes it to vary the position of the rack – so varying the volume of fuel supplied to the injectors and the power and speed of the engine.

The opening pressure depends upon the speed of the gear pump which in turn depends upon the speed of the engine. Note that engines fitted with this type of governor will probably be difficult to start by hand cranking as the pump will not provide a pressure high enough to move the rack into the maximum delivery position. The closing

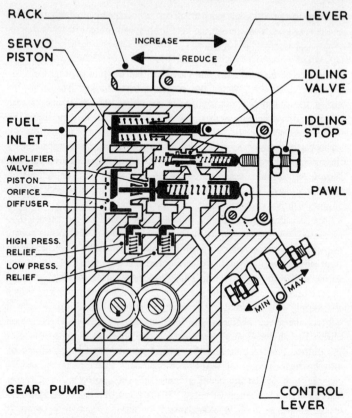

Fig. 2.17   Hydraulic governor

pressure depends upon the rate of flow of fuel through the amplifier valve. The valve is forced towards its seat by a spring-loaded plunger, which is itself loaded by a control pawl secured to the control lever connected to the accelerator pedal. The valve is forced away from its seat when the movement of the amplifier piston is large enough and strong enough. This movement is due to the varying pressure difference between the two sides of the piston, the fuel flowing through an orifice in the piston producing a pressure drop behind the head which increases as the rate of flow increases, i.e. as pump speed increases.

Operation

Starting. The pedal is fully depressed to load the plunger and hold the amplifier to its seat. When the engine is first cranked by the starter motor the pump delivers fuel to the amplifier and servo pistons. As the pressure difference across the amplifier piston is very small the piston cannot open the valve, and as the opening pressure is low the servo piston cannot be moved by it. As continued cranking increases the opening pressure, the servo piston is forced outward and the rack is moved into the maximum fuel-delivery position. The amplifier piston remains closed. The engine then fires and runs up to speed. As the engine begins to run under its own power its light loading results in its speed increasing, and this increases the speed of the pump. The increased flow of fuel produces an increased pressure difference across the amplifier piston, which therefore moves to open the amplifier valve. Fuel now passes through the valve and closing pressure acts at the spring side of the servo piston. This pressure assists the spring in opposing the opening pressure and the servo piston is forced inward to reduce the supply of fuel. When the pedal is released the idling valve will control the speed of the engine by varying the size of a bleed which allows fuel under closing pressure to escape back to the intake side of the pump. The opening and the closing pressures are both limited by valves which open to allow fuel to escape back to the pump.

Accelerating. When the pedal is depressed, the control pawl increases the loading of the amplifier valve. This reduces the flow of fuel passing to the spring side of the servo piston, while the opening pressure is increased by the continued pump delivery. The servo piston is therefore moved to increase the fuel supply, and the engine power and speed are increased in proportion to the pedal movement.

Governing. As the engine reaches the speed set by the pedal, the amplifier valve is opened by the amplifier piston. The closing pressure is increased and the servo piston is moved until a position of balance is reached. At this point the fuel supply is correct for the preset speed of the engine. If the load on the engine increases for any reason, the reduction of its speed will result in a reduced flow of fuel from the pump. The matching reduced pressure difference across the amplifier piston will reduce its thrust on the amplifier valve and it will be closed slightly. This increases the opening pressure and the servo piston is moved to increase the fuel supply until the preset speed is regained. If the load on the engine should be reduced the increase in the speed of the engine will produce an increased flow of fuel from the pump. The resulting increased pressure difference across the amplifier piston will increase its thrust on the amplifier valve and it will be opened slightly. This reduces the opening pressure, and the servo piston will move the rack to reduce the fuel supply until the engine speed falls back to its preset speed.

Maximum speed limitation. When the pedal is fully depressed, the control pawl loads the amplifier valve to the maximum permitted by the control stop. As the power and speed of the engine increase the servo piston is moved outward until a point of balance is reached. At this point, determined by the stop, the fuel supply will be such that the power and speed of the engine can increase no further.

Shut off. A positive fuel-shut-off control is incorporated which moves the rack into the zero delivery position irrespective of the position of any of the other controls.

THE INJECTOR

Function

The injector is used to introduce fuel under pressure into the highly compressed, heated, and turbulent charge of air in the combustion chamber. The pressure must be high enough to ensure (a) the adequate atomization of the liquid fuel and (b) the production of a spray or sprays of atomized fuel of the correct reach (penetration) and of the correct shape (pattern). The spray must also be directed to the required portion of the combustion chamber.

Construction (Figure 2.18)

The injector consists of (a) a nozzle and (b) a nozzle holder. The nozzle consists of a needle valve and seat, the valve being held to its seat by a spring-loading mechanism fitted inside the nozzle holder. The spring tension may be adjusted by shims, or by a screw and locknut. The nozzle holder is clamped to, or screwed into, the cylinder head and the holders used for injectors for direct-injection types of combustion chamber usually include edge-type filters. These filters trap particles of scale detached from the delivery pipes and retain them until fuel pulsation has broken them down small enough to pass through the nozzle holes without fear of blockage. The holder has connection for the delivery pipe and a leak-off pipe.

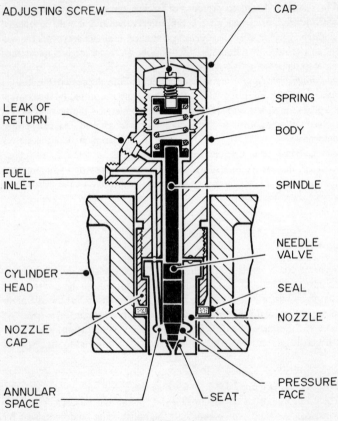

Fig. 2.18   Injector

The nozzle is usually secured to its holder by a screwed nozzle cap, and it may be dowelled to ensure its correct location. It is most important that only the correct torque loadings be used when refitting the cap, and when fitting the injector to the cylinder head. The nozzle and its holder are drilled to direct the high-pressure fuel from the delivery pipe to the annular space at the lower end of the nozzle.

Operation

When the standing pressure in the delivery pipe and the injector is exceeded by the pressure built up in the chamber of the injection pump the delivery valve of the pump is forced away from its seat. The higher pressure acts immediately in the annular space of the injector and, by acting on the face of the needle valve, produces a force which tends to lift the valve away from its seat. When this force exceeds that applied to the valve by the spring, the valve moves away from its seat, and atomized fuel is sprayed into the combustion chamber.

When the continued movement of the pump plunger results in the uncovering of its spill port the pressure in the pump chamber immediately collapses. The injector needle is immediately returned to its seat by its spring, and the closing of the pump delivery valve by its spring ensures that fuel, under a pressure just less than that required for injection, is trapped in the pipe line and injector body.

NOTE. Excessive tension at the injector spring will cause a slight delay of the timing of injection and vice versa.

NOZZLE TYPES

The two main types of nozzle in service are the hole types and the pintle types.

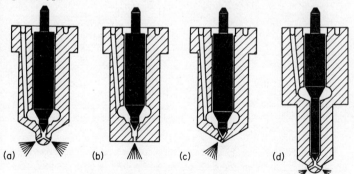

Fig. 2.19   Hole-type nozzles (from *left*: four-hole, single-hole, single-side, long-stem)

Hole types (Figure 2.19)

These are used in conjunction with direct-injection combustion chambers. They may be of the normal or of the long-stem type, the latter being used where either space is restricted or heat may become excessive. Single-hole types may have the hole axis coincident with the axis of the needle or at right angles to it. In multi-hole types the holes are so arranged as to provide a symmetrical pattern of sprays. Four holes are commonly used but some nozzles may have up to twelve holes. The size and length of the hole determine the shape and penetration of the spray, the holes varying in diameter from 0·2 mm upward in steps of 0·02 mm.

Pintle nozzles (Figure 2.20)

These are used in conjunction with separate-chamber or indirect-injection types of combustion chamber – which always have adequate air turbulence. In pintle nozzles the lower part of the needle valve, below the sealing face, is of a special shape and protrudes through the single hole. The shape and size of this projection or pintle determines the shape and reach of the spray.

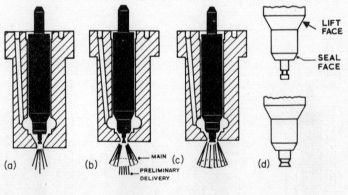

Fig. 2.20   Pintle nozzles

In some types the shape of the pintle is such that the slight movement of the valve results in the delivery of a preliminary spray – the main delivery being slightly delayed although the timing of injection is not late. The use of delay nozzles results in a more gradual pressure rise in the combustion chamber and therefore more even combustion and smoother engine running.

Cooled nozzles (Figure 2.21)
In very large engines which use heavier fuels, it may be necessary to cool the nozzles. This usually involves the jacketing of the nozzles to allow their cooling to be carried out by the circulation of fuel, a separate ducting system being arranged between the fuel inlet connection and the leak-off connection.

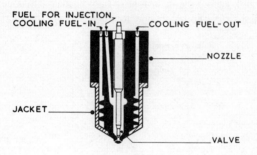

Fig. 2.21   Cooled nozzles

Pintaux nozzle (Figure 2.23)
In indirect-injection combustion chambers the region of highest temperature at normal engine speeds lies off centre and opposite the entry.

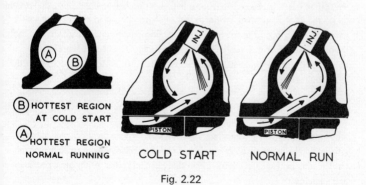

Fig. 2.22

At engine cranking speeds, however, the region of highest temperature is at the opposite side of the chamber near the entry. Difficult cold starting results, therefore, if the more usual type of pintle nozzle is employed.

The Pintaux nozzle is a special type of pintle nozzle which provides easier cold starting by delivering main and pilot sprays in different directions governed by the speed of lift of the needle valve. The valve is so shaped and arranged that when it is lifted slowly, i.e. at starter-motor cranking speed, about 90% of the delivery is made via the oblique hole before the main hole is fully opened. The main delivery is directed to the hottest region to provide easier starting while the

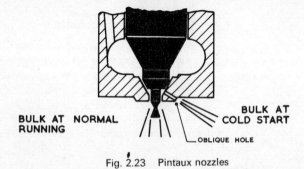

BULK AT NORMAL RUNNING   BULK AT COLD START

OBLIQUE HOLE

Fig. 2.23   Pintaux nozzles

pilot delivery completes the heating of the air charge. At normal engine speeds, pressure is built up faster in the injection pump and the valve therefore has a quicker lift. There is only time for a small pilot delivery to be made through the oblique hole before the main delivery is made through the main hole to the hottest region now located away from the throat. The pilot delivery assists in reducing the rate of pressure rise in the chamber and so reduces combustion knock and provides smoother running.

NOZZLE TESTING

The manufacturers' detailed instructions must be adhered to, but generally the tests must ensure that (a) the valve seat is pressure tight, (b) there is no excessive leak-off and (c) atomization and spray patterns are satisfactory.

Nozzle tests

When a C.I. engine fails to run smoothly the cause is most likely to be the faulty action of one or more of the injectors. The faulty one can be located by running the engine and slackening off each delivery-pipe union in turn at the pump end (similar to shorting out the spark plugs in a spark-ignition engine). The faulty injector is the one which produces no change in the running of the engine when its delivery union is slackened off. Once located, the injector may be tested by either operating it on its own delivery pipe or, better, operating it in a special test rig.

Test on own pipe

(1) Disconnect all the other delivery pipes at the pump to avoid the flooding of the combustion chambers.

(2) Turn the engine by hand with the injector connected to the pump but not fitted into the cylinder head. Examine the spray pattern, being very careful to keep the hands and face well clear of the spray. A serviceable nozzle should grunt when operated, and sprays in single-hole types should be symmetrical. Multi-hole types should give sprays which are all of the same shape and reach, and which are symmetrical about the axis. The most usual cause of distorted patterns of spray is dirt or carbon around or in the spray holes, or carbon on the needle-valve seat. This can be remedied by cleaning with the proper tools.

Test in a test rig

The instructions of the manufacturer must be adhered to, but in general the tests carried out should ensure that (a) the needle valve and seat are pressure tight, (b) the joint face is pressure tight, (c) the operating pressure is correct and (d) the spray is of the correct shape and the fuel is properly atomized.

The rig (Fig. 2.24) consists of a small fuel tank and a paper-element filter, a hand-operated pump, a pressure gauge, and a spray chamber in which the spray can be properly and safely observed.

The injector is fitted into the spray chamber and connected to the delivery pipe of the pump. The pump is operated a few times with the air vent open and the gauge inoperative to expel air before the tests are carried out.

The first test is for back leakage. The pressure gauge is brought into

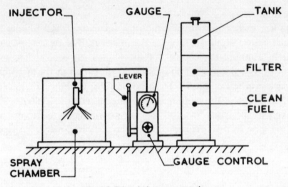

Fig. 2.24   Injector test rig

action by opening its control valve, and the opening pressure of the injector needle valve is adjusted to between 160 bar and 170 bar ($16000 \, kN/m^2$ and $17000 \, kN/m^2$). Pressure is built up sufficiently to open the valve and is then built up again to just under the set pressure. The time is then measured for the pressure to fall from 150 bar to 100 bar ($15000 \, kN/m^2$ to $10000 \, kN/m^2$). This drop in pressure should not take less than 6 seconds for a serviceable nozzle of the hole type. The pressures for the pintle type are from 100 bar to 75 bar ($10000 \, kN/m^2$ to $7500 \, kN/m^2$). Pintaux nozzles require the use of a special adaptor and a different form of test. Leakage must not be found during this test if the nozzle is to be considered serviceable. External signs will be observed at the thread of the cap nut and it must be corrected by stripping the unit and cleaning the joint faces. If the time is still too short when tested after cleaning, and there is no sign of external leakage, pressure is escaping up the side of the valve, and the nozzle should be replaced.

The second test is for the pressure setting. The pump lever is forced down slowly and the gauge observed carefully to determine the highest pressure indicated before the valve lifts – this being shown by the flick of the gauge needle. Adjustments may be made by means of a screw and locknut or by shims.

The third test is for seat pressure tightness, and the pressure is built up to about 10 bar ($1000 \, kN/m^2$) less than that used in the first test. At this pressure the tip of the nozzle or its flat face must remain dry. There must be no drip or seepage of fuel.

The final test is for spray. The pump must be operated at about 100 strokes per minute and the sprays should be properly atomized, i.e. even-sized droplets throughout and of the same reach. They must all be symmetrical about their axis.

Nozzle cleaning

This should only be carried out in a room properly fitted out to ensure absolute cleanliness.

(1) Remove nozzle cap in special jig and lift out nozzle and valve. Take great care not to damage their ground surfaces. Wash in fuel oil or Shell Fusus A. Wash the injector holder.

(2) Rinse the nozzle and valve in clean and *filtered* oil and try the valve in the nozzle. If it can be rotated by the finger tips without sticking or rattling it is serviceable. Wash all the joint faces again with filtered oil and assemble the nozzle to the holder. Tighten the nozzle cap to the correct torque loading in the jig. Use only the special tools.

(3) After test, fit back into the cylinder head with a new gasket.

Table 2.1   Fault diagnosis

Fault	Causes	Remedies
1. Nozzle does not buzz (Note that delay types may not on test rig)	Valve binding or seat leakage	Remove, clean, refit and test nozzle, replace
	Cap nut distorted	Replace – correct torque loading
2. Leak-off excessive	Excessively worn valve and bore	Replace nozzle assembly
	Dirt between face of nozzle and holder	Strip, clean and refit
	Slack nozzle cap	Tighten to correct torque loading
3. Blued nozzle	Excessive tightening of holder	Remove, fit new seal washer, correct torque loading
	Excessive cap loading	Correct loading
	Engine overheating	Locate cause and correct
4. Injection pressure too high	Spring tension too great	Adjust and test
	Valve seized	Replace valve and nozzle or clean
	Blocked nozzle holes	Clean with correct tools

Fault	Causes	Remedies
5. Injection pressure too low	Spring tension inadequate	Adjust and test
	Spring broken	Fit new spring and adjust
6. Nozzle drip	Valve sticking Carbon deposits	Strip, clean, refit, or replace
7. Distorted spray	Holes partly blocked Carbon at valve tip Pintle damaged	Clean with correct tools Clean nozzle Replace nozzle assembly

3 The DPA Injection Pump

In the distributor-type injection pumps the metering and pressurizing of every delivery is made by the same components. The deliveries to the different injectors are therefore made the same volume automatically, and the pump does not have to be calibrated after its initial assembly. The intervals between the deliveries are determined by the mechanical spacing of ports, and the deliveries are produced by accurately machined cams. Correct phasing is therefore automatic and does not need checking in service.

These pumps have no heavily stressed components, and the size and weight of the pumps are virtually the same no matter how many injectors they have to supply. Injection timing can be varied, where required, by the incorporation of an automatic advance-and-retard mechanism. Accurate speed control is maintained throughout the whole speed range by either a mechanical or a hydraulic governor. Vehicle engines are usually fitted with the hydraulically governed pumps while tractors and electrical generating sets, which require closer control, are fitted with mechanically governed pumps. The pumps are filled with fuel oil under pressure, so all parts are very fully lubricated and air and dirt are excluded.

HYDRAULICALLY GOVERNED TYPE

Construction (Figure 3.1)
The pump is timed to, and driven by, the engine. The drive shaft of the pump rotates at half engine speed in four-stroke engines and is connected to a cylindrical rotor which is a close fit in the pump body or hydraulic head (Fig. 3.2). The head has one inlet port and the same number of outlet ports as the engine has injectors. The rotor has a central bore with the same number of transverse inlet ports spaced at equal angles which align in turn with the inlet port of the head. The

54

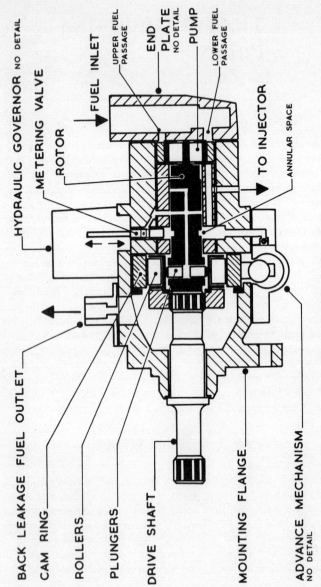

Fig. 3.1   DPA injection pump

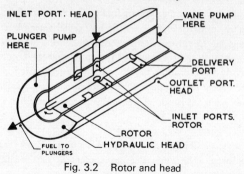

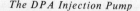

Fig. 3.2   Rotor and head

rotor also has one distribution or delivery port which comes into alignment with each of the outlet ports in the head in firing sequence.

Two opposed plungers reciprocate in transverse bores at the driven end of the rotor. These plungers are forced outward by fuel from the central bore, and inward by the lobes of a stationary cam ring (see Fig. 3.3). The ring is fitted in the hydraulic head and has the same number of lobes as the engine has injectors. The distance the plungers are forced outward is determined by the volume of fuel entering the rotor, and this in turn is determined by the combination of (a) the pressure of the fuel entering the rotor, (b) the volume passing through the metering port controlled by the governor and (c) the time for which the inlet port in the head coincides with an inlet port in the rotor.

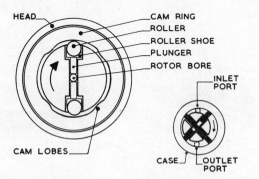

Fig. 3.3   Pressure pump   Fig. 3.4   Transfer pump

The rotor drives a vane type of fuel transfer pump (Fig. 3.4) which places the fuel under transfer pressure before delivering it to the metering and regulating valves. The metering valve and port are arranged about half-way along the length of the rotor and the regulating valve is arranged in the end plate of the head. Fuel from the lift pump and main filter enters the pump at the end plate and a back-leakage pipe returns fuel from the inside of the pump to the main filter.

Operation (Figures 3.5, 3.6 and 3.7)

Delivery pressure. The engine-driven lift pump draws fuel from the tank and forces it through the paper element of the main filter at delivery pressure. Fuel in excess of requirements, and any air, is returned to the tank via a restricting orifice in the filter head. The filtered fuel then passes to the injection pump, entering the end plate via a nylon filter and flowing through an upper fuel passage into the chamber of the transfer pump.

Transfer pressure. The transfer pump increases the pressure on the fuel and forces it, under transfer pressure, through a lower fuel passage to an annular groove in the outside of the rotor. This groove communicates with the bore of the hollow metering valve (governor) and the pressure is reduced slightly as the fuel passes through the valve. The reduced pressure is known as metering pressure.

Metering pressure. Fuel under metering pressure passes from the metering valve to the inlet port in the head, via the oblique metering

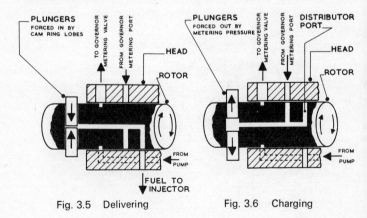

Fig. 3.5   Delivering   Fig. 3.6   Charging

port. When one of the inlet ports of the rotor sweeps opposite the inlet port of the head, fuel under metering pressure flows into the central bore of the rotor – charging the rotor pump by forcing the two plungers to move out from the centre. Further rotation of the rotor closes the inlet port and seals the fuel inside the rotor.

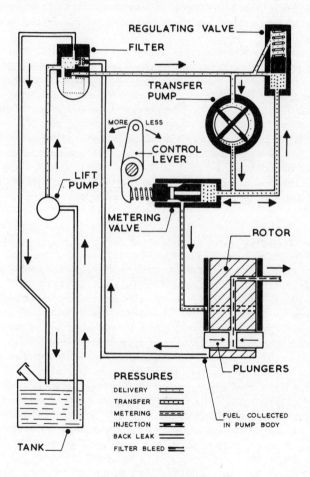

Fig. 3.7   Operation

Injection pressure. As the motion of the rotor continues, its distributor port uncovers one of the outlet ports in the head. At the exact moment of port opening the plungers are forced inward by the lobes of the cam ring – and the metered quantity of fuel is forced through the port into the pipe line of the injector under a very high pressure. The sudden pressure increase forces the needle valve of the injector to lift from its seat and the metered quantity of fuel is sprayed into the combustion chamber.

Unloading pressure. The rapid closing of the injector needle valve of the injector which is essential to avoid 'dribble' is obtained through cam retraction. The lobes of the cam ring are so shaped that just as the plungers complete their inward movement they can immediately move out a very slight distance. This movement occurs just before the distributor port is closed and allows a drop in pressure just sufficient to enable the needle valve to close in one swift movement. Pressure slightly below that needed for injection is maintained in the pipe lines and injector bodies.

Further rotation of the rotor uncovers the next rotor inlet port and the sequence of operations is repeated for the next injector in firing order.

The governor

Construction (Figure 3.8)

The main feature of this simple governor is the metering valve. This valve alters the area of the metering port at the upper end of the inlet port in the hydraulic head. The valve is cylindrical and has an annular groove in its outer face. The lower part is drilled axially and radially to permit fuel to pass through it from the annular groove of the rotor to the inlet port of the head. The upper face of the groove may be chamfered to ease the rate of change in the area of the metering port. This helps to provide smoother idling speeds. The lower side of the valve is subjected to fuel transfer pressure which tends to force the valve upward to close the port. The governor control spring tends to force the valve down to open the port.

The control spring is loaded by a rack-and-pinion mechanism operated by the accelerator pedal. At a given pedal position the spring loading on the valve is balanced by the transfer pressure – and the valve takes up a position where it allows the passage of the correct quantity of fuel for that particular engine speed.

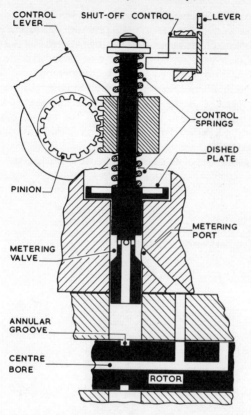

Fig. 3.8   Hydraulic governor

Operation

If the pedal position is unchanged but the load against which the engine is working is increased, engine speed will be reduced. The transfer pressure will also be reduced and the control spring will be able to move the metering valve down. The area of the metering port will be increased, more fuel will be injected, and the engine will develop more power and regain its preset speed.

If the pedal position is unchanged but the load on the engine is reduced, engine speed will increase. The transfer pressure will also increase and it will cause the metering valve to move upward and reduce the area of the metering port. Less fuel will be injected, the engine will develop less power, and the engine speed will fall back to the preset speed.

Dashpot. Under light engine loads the transfer pressure tends to fluctuate and this causes the metering valve to flutter. The rapid and small movements of the valve are damped down by the action of the dished washer attached to the valve stem. The washer moves in a shallow bore and, as the interior of the pump is filled by fuel, a dashpot effect is produced.

Stopping control. The rack of the pedal control mechanism can slide on the valve stem and is arranged between the control spring and the

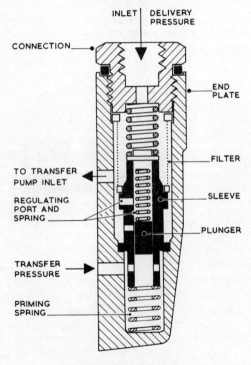

Fig. 3.9   Regulating valve

shut-off spring. When the shut-off control is operated the lever raises the shut-off cam, which in turn lifts the washer secured to the top of the valve stem. The metering valve is therefore lifted to close the metering port, and injection ceases as the pump plungers stay in the retracted position. The shut-off control can be operated irrespective of the position of the pedal rack.

Detail

Regulating valve (Figure 3.9)

The regulating valve is arranged in parallel with the transfer pump in the hydraulic circuit. Its purpose is to maintain a pre-determined relationship between the speed of rotor rotation and the transfer pressure. The valve consists of a plunger which moves inside a sleeve, the plunger being forced upward by transfer pressure and down by the combination of the force of a spring and the fuel delivery pressure.

As transfer pressure increases with the speed of rotation of the rotor the plunger is moved upward to uncover the regulating port. This movement allows fuel to escape back to the inlet side of the transfer pump in controlled quantities – so regulating the transfer pressure. The area of the regulating port and the strength of the spring are designed to suit particular engines.

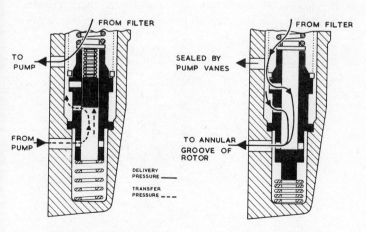

Fig. 3.10   Regulating   Fig. 3.11   Priming

Priming

Fuel cannot pass through the transfer pump (to the upper fuel passage and the inlet port in the hydraulic head) unless the pump is operating. When the lift pump is operated by its priming lever, fuel under delivery pressure forces the regulating plunger to move down. This action compresses the priming spring under the plunger and uncovers two holes in the sleeve which communicate with the lower fuel passage. The fuel then by-passes the transfer pump and primes the injection pump.

When the engine is cranked by the starter motor the transfer pressure forces the regulator plunger to move upward and so close off the priming ports.

Lubrication

A controlled quantity of fuel under transfer pressure is allowed to escape continuously into the body of the unit. The unit is therefore filled by fuel at all times and all parts, including the governor mechanism, are automatically lubricated. Excess fuel is returned continuously to the main filter.

Cam and plungers (Figures 3.12 and 3.13)

The cam ring does not rotate, although it may be turned slightly in some pumps by the advance-and-retard mechanism. The outer end of each pump plunger contacts its own roller shoe and roller. The shoes have specially shaped lugs which pass through and contact eccentric

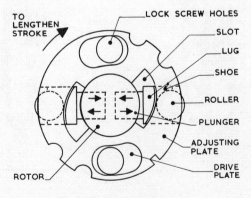

Fig. 3.12   Stroke adjustment

slots in an adjuster plate secured to the cam driving plate. The position of the adjusting plate on the driving plate determines the maximum possible length of stroke which can be made by the plungers.

The rollers do not contact the base of the cam ring between the

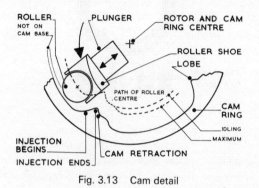

Fig. 3.13   Cam detail

lobes. The lobes are so shaped as to force the plungers inward very quickly at the exact moment when the distributor port of the rotor uncovers an outlet port in the head. They are also shaped to then allow the plungers to move out again very slightly just before the port is closed – to drop the line pressure to reduce injector dribble.

The length of stroke varies and depends upon the quantity of fuel which enters the rotor during its charging operation, being least at idling speed and greatest at maximum speed.

Advance and retard (Figure 3.14)
This mechanism is arranged below the cam ring. A ball-shaped pin is screwed into the cam ring and is arranged between a piston and a plunger inside a sealed cylinder. The plunger is forced inward by two coil springs, and the piston by transfer pressure supplied from the annular groove of the rotor.

An increase in engine speed produces an increase in transfer pressure which forces the piston to move inward. This action turns the cam ring and compresses the springs in the plunger. In this way the timing of injection can be advanced by up to about 9°.

A non-return ball valve is fitted between the piston and the annular groove and this allows fuel to enter the cylinder only. The ball is held

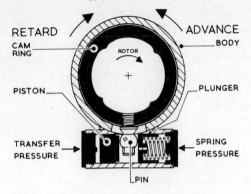

Fig. 3.14   Advance and retard

to its seat during injection and so locks the cam ring. A controlled leakage of fuel past the piston allows the plunger springs to return the cam ring and the piston when the speed of the engine is reduced – so retarding the moment of injection.

MECHANICALLY GOVERNED TYPE

The construction and operation of the hydraulic components of the two forms of DPA injection pump are almost the same. A small difference is that in the mechanically governed type the area of the metering port is varied by the partial rotation of the metering valve in its bore instead by its up and down movement.

In mechanical construction the body of the mechanically governed form is extended to accommodate the flyweights and sleeve of the governor, and its upper surface is machined flat to provide a mounting for the control mechanism. The drive shaft is detachable and is known as a quill shaft. In both forms the drive shaft has a master spline which is used when timing the pump to the engine.

The Mechanical Governor
Construction (Figure 3.15)

This governor, like its hydraulic counterpart, controls the power and speed of the engine at every point on its speed range, i.e. both are all speed governors. The mechanical governor consists of a flyweight mechanism, a lever and spring control mechanism, and the metering valve and port. The top of the metering valve is secured to the centre of its lever.

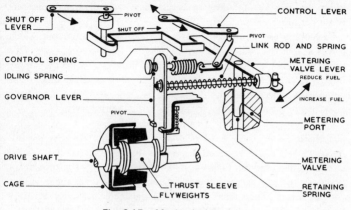

Fig. 3.15   Mechanical governor

The flyweight mechanism consists of six identical flyweights which are arranged at equal intervals around a thrust sleeve, the flyweights pivoting on a shoulder at the drive end of the sleeve and being enclosed by a cage. The cage and the flyweights are rotated by the drive shaft, and the movements of the flyweights, due to the action of centrifugal force, cause the movement of the thrust sleeve along the drive shaft against the spring loading of a governor lever.

The movements of the sleeve are transmitted to the lower end of this governor lever. The lever is held to a pivot by a restraining spring, and the upper end of the lever is connected to the lever of the metering valve by a link rod. The rod passes through the governor lever and a long spring, the full extension of the spring being prevented by a locknut and a plain washer on the end of the link rod.

The governor lever is also connected to the control lever, operated by the accelerator pedal, through two springs. The much larger governor spring is arranged at the valve side of the governor lever and the smaller idling spring at the flyweight side, the two being connected by a large-headed pin. The pin passes through the idling spring and the governor lever, the governor spring being hooked through it at one end. The opposite end of this spring is attached to the pedal control lever. The movement of the pedal therefore varies the load applied by this spring to the governor lever. At idling speeds the governor spring is coil bound and only the idling spring is in operation. At all speeds above idling the idling spring is fully compressed and only the governor spring is in operation.

The operation of the shut-off lever turns an eccentric pin which forces a lever to contact and turn the lever of the metering valve. This turns the valve to close the metering port and so shut off the supply of fuel to the rotor. During this action the spring on the link rod is compressed and this allows the fuel to be shut-off irrespective of the positions of the governor lever and the pedal control lever.

Operation

Starting. When the accelerator pedal is fully depressed the control lever is turned until it contacts its maximum speed stop. This movement first fully compresses the idling spring, and then extends the governor control spring which turns the lever of the metering valve and fully opens the metering port. When the starter motor is energized the injectors will receive the maximum possible quantity of fuel and the engine will start and run up to speed. If the pedal is not released, the light loading of the engine will result in its speed increasing. The flyweights will be forced outward and the thrust sleeve will tilt the governor lever about its pivot. The lever, acting through the link rod, will then turn the metering valve to reduce the area of the metering port – so reducing the quantity of fuel passing to the injectors and therefore reducing the power and speed of the engine.

Idling. If the pedal is then released the governor lever will take up a position determined by the balance between the forces due to thrust sleeve and the idling spring. The resulting movement of the link rod and the metering valve will then provide the correct quantity of fuel for idling speed, the control lever being held against the adjustable idling-speed stop.

Accelerating. As the pedal is progressively depressed the idling spring is depressed and the governor spring progressively extended. This causes the governor lever to tilt and the link-rod spring to move the metering valve to progressively open the metering port. The injectors receive greater quantities of fuel, and the engine produces more power and increases its speed.

Governing. If the pedal position is held but the loading of the engine is reduced, engine speed will increase. Under these conditions the flyweights will move outward, the governor lever will tilt, and the link rod will draw back the valve lever – reducing the fuel supply until the engine returns to its preset speed. If the pedal position is held but the loading of the engine is increased, engine speed will be reduced. The flyweights will move inward, the governor lever will be tilted in the opposite direction, and the link-rod spring will move the valve to supply more fuel until the engine regains its preset speed.

Timing to engine

The drive shafts of both forms of DPA pump have a master spline which is engaged with a master spline in the engine coupling. The bolt holes in the mounting flange are elongated to permit a slight amount of movement about the axis of the drive shaft.

In some mechanically governed pumps the quill shaft is replaced by a keyed drive hub which is bolted to the engine coupling. In some hydraulically governed pumps a flat torsion bar is fitted between the end of the rotor and the pump drive coupling. This bar runs through the centre of the shaft and is designed to absorb backlash in the shaft. *Procedure*. Timing procedures vary between different make and models of engine and the instructions of the manufacturer must be correctly carried out. A rule-of-thumb method – which should only be used until such time as the correct procedure can be carried out – is:

(1) Align the master spline on the drive shaft of the pump with the master spline in the engine coupling, and engage the pump with the engine.

(2) Force the mounting flange of the pump into contact with the flange on the engine, and tighten the bolts until they just grip.

(3) Turn the pump body in the slotted bolt holes until the timing marks on the pump coincide with those on the engine flange. Fully tighten the bolts.

(4) Connect the fuel inlet pipe to the end plate of the pump, and the **leak-back pipe to the connection near the pump flange. Connect** the two control levers to their linkage and check that each has its full range of movement. Take particular care that pedal pressure is not transmitted to the maximum speed stop of the pump lever (check vehicle manual for the correct adjustment of the pedal limiting stop).

(5) Fill and prime the pump before attempting to start the engine.

Priming

Priming and venting should only be necessary when a pump has been replaced or the system has been opened for any reason, e.g. for the fitting of a new filter element. It will be necessary if the system has been drained by running out of fuel. Before the following operations are carried out the outside of all vent screws and connections which are to be opened or slackened off, and their surrounding areas, must be thoroughly cleaned.

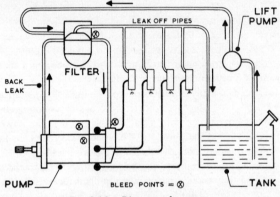

Fig. 3.16   Diagram of system

(1) Slacken either the filter outlet connection or the pump inlet connection – according to which is at the higher level. Operate the lift pump by its priming lever and allow fuel to escape until no more air bubbles can be observed. Tighten the connection. Four-boss filters must always be vented at their plugged boss.

(2) Slacken the vent screws on the governor housing and on the hydraulic head. Operate the lift pump by the priming lever until fuel free from air flows. Tighten the housing vent screw before the governor vent screw.

(3) Check that the shut-off control is in the 'run' position. Set the pedal control to its fully open position. Slacken two injector pipe connections at the injector ends. Crank the engine until fuel flows free of air. Tighten the connections.

NOTE. When a replacement pump has been fitted the idling and maximum speed stops must be adjusted according to the instructions given in the manual of the engine manufacturer.

4 Carburation

The air consumed by the engine must be kept free from dust in order to prolong the life of the pistons, piston rings, and cylinder bores. The cleaners used are mounted on the main air tube of the carburettor and are usually of the oiled-mesh or paper-element type. They are often combined with some form of air silencer.

The noise produced in the intake system is due to the vibration of columns of air and is known as resonance. The silencers damp down the frequency of these vibrations to a level which the human ear cannot detect, and they usually consist of tubes which are tuned to a particular intake system.

Cleaner and silencer (Figure 4.1)
In these types the air passes through oiled wire mesh before passing through tuned resonator tubes to the carburettor. The particles of dust are trapped and retained by the oiled wire mesh while the resonator tubes damp down the sound. The mesh should be washed in petrol and re-oiled at 8000 km intervals or less if operating conditions are very

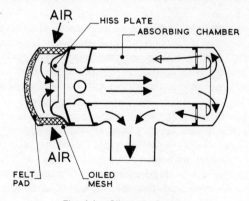

Fig. 4.1   Silencer—cleaner

poor. In some types the cleaner draws air from the rocker box cover which keeps the mesh wet with oil mist and also helps to ventilate the sump.

Paper-element cleaner (Figure 4.2)

In these types the air is drawn through a long tube into a shallow cylindrical casing. The air is then drawn through a filter of special paper, which retains any dust, before passing into the main air tube of the carburettor. The filter element is sealed into the casing and must be replaced at specified intervals. In order to offer the least

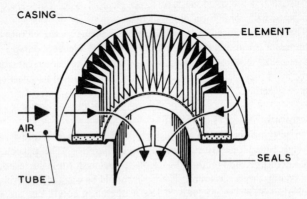

Fig. 4.2   Paper-element cleaner (upper seal and top removed)

possible restriction to the flow of the air, the area of the filter must be relatively large, yet it must fit into a small space. This is possible because the paper is folded into pleats and then coiled into a spiral where it is retained by card collars. Rubber or paper sealing discs are used to provide an airtight seal to the bottom and cover of the casing.

Oil-bath type (Figure 4.3)

These are very efficient but they have the disadvantages of being both large and heavy. They must be well supported or they may fracture the carburettor casting, particularly on modern engines with low rubber mountings and high-mounted carburettors. These types may also be used with C.I. engines and in some forms may be mounted on the roof of the driver's cab.

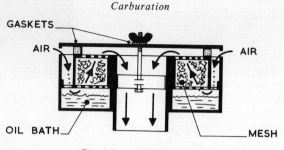

Fig. 4.3   Oil-bath cleaner

The air enters at the side of the cleaner and has to change its direction very sharply. This causes the heavier particles of dust to strike the surface of the oil and sink to the bottom of the oil tray. The air then passes up through the wire mesh where the lighter dust particles are trapped by the oil on the mesh. Oil is continually splashed up by engine vibration, and this washes the dust out of the mesh into the tray and keeps the mesh wet. The filter should be washed out and filled with clean oil at about 4000-km intervals and new gaskets fitted.

NOTE. Modern carburettors supply air to the float chamber via a duct from the main air tube so that only clean air can enter the float chamber as petrol is withdrawn from it.

INLET MANIFOLDS

The inlet manifold has to be so designed that it provides the best possible combination of equal mixture distribution between the cylinders, and equal mixture strengths delivered to each cylinder. Even in a well designed and tested manifold, some cylinders receive a weaker mixture than others – and the overall mixture strength has to be increased to enable the weaker cylinders to produce their proper power output.

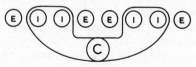

SINGLE CARBURETTOR   GROUPED INLET PORTS

Fig. 4.4   Four-cylinder porting

An essential feature of the inlet manifold is its ability to maintain the atomized drops of liquid petrol in suspension in the air as the mixture flows through the manifold. This is influenced by:

(a) The degree of atomization of the petrol by the carburettor.

(b) The degree of depression in the manifold.

(c) The temperature of the mixture in the manifold.

Other design features include:

(1) The bore must be of such diameter as to maintain a fairly high mixture speed at low engine speeds. It must be fairly smooth but not polished, and of the same diameter as the main air tube of the carburettor at all points. Sharp bends must be avoided and as few bends as possible employed. These features are important in reducing losses in mixture velocity which reduce the weight of mixture induced.

(2) A length of bore such that the natural fluctuations in mixture flow tend to increase the weight of mixture induced at all engine speeds.

(3) An arrangement whereby the manifold walls only may be heated.

Manifold heating

Although a few inlet manifolds are formed in the cylinder head, or have their own water jackets, most inlet manifolds are heated by the exhaust manifold. Usually the two are bolted together at a point opposite from the mixture intake and the heat is applied to a very small area. This feature is known as hot spotting.

Inlet manifolds are usually castings of malleable iron or aluminium alloy and the carburettor is bolted to a flange to form a downdraught, semi-downdraught, or sidedraught inlet system. The downdraught system helps provide the highest Volumetric Efficiency but it has the following disadvantages:

(1) Wet mixtures are delivered at low air speeds, i.e. atomization is coarse.

(2) Liquid petrol collects in the lower parts of the manifold when the vehicle is on a gradient – resulting in very rich mixtures entering the rear cylinders. These tend to wash away the lubricating oil and increase the rate of wear.

(3) Liquid petrol collects in the manifold during cold starting.

These disadvantages are overcome by the use of special types of hot spot.

Well-type hot spot (Figure 4.5)

In these types the liquid petrol is collected in a well formed in the manifold below the carburettor. The floor of the well consists of a copper plate which is heated by the exhaust gases. When the engine is cold some of the liquid petrol passes directly out of the manifold via the drain pipe. As the engine warms up the copper plate is heated by the exhaust gases and the remaining petrol is vaporized. The difference between atmospheric pressure and the depression in the manifold forces air to pass up the drain pipe and through the well into the manifold, carrying with it the vaporized petrol. Wet mixtures are thus reduced, and the small and constant air leak is compensated by the adjustment of the carburettor.

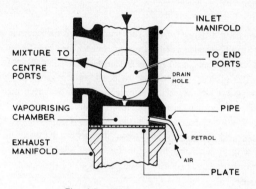

Fig. 4.5   Well-type hot spot

In order to reduce the effect of the air leak at engine idling speeds the drain pipe is usually of small bore, or is fitted with a restrictor. In some designs the lower end of the pipe may be fitted with a small non-return valve which is automatically closed by the pressure difference at engine idling speeds.

Controlled type (Figure 4.6)

In these types the intake manifold is jacketed under the carburettor. When the engine is cold a thermostatically controlled valve directs the exhaust gases through and around the jacket, the heat vaporizing any liquid petrol and reducing wet mixtures. As the engine warms up the valve is moved to reduce the flow of gases through the jacket until

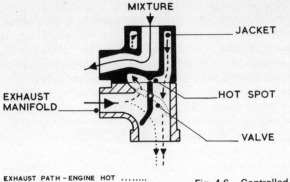

MIXTURE

JACKET

EXHAUST
MANIFOLD

HOT SPOT

VALVE

EXHAUST PATH - ENGINE HOT ....
EXHAUST PATH - ENGINE COLD _ _ _ _

Fig. 4.6   Controlled type

none is passing through when the engine is at its normal operating temperature. The valve is often connected to the throttle to provide a fast, cold idling speed, and it is so arranged that at full throttle it opens to allow the greater part of the exhaust gas to pass directly to the exhaust pipe – even when the engine is cold. The valve movement is controlled by a spiral bimetal strip, the valve being attached to the inner end while the outer end is attached to a pin on the exhaust manifold. Brass and steel strips are secured together by brazing, and the spiral is wound with the brass on the outer side so that the greater expansion of the brass results in the inner end of the spiral turning the valve spindle.

EXHAUST MANIFOLD (Figure 4.7)

The exhaust manifold may be a malleable iron casting or a welded assembly of steel pipes and flanges. It must be so designed that the flow of exhaust gases from one cylinder cannot obstruct the flow of

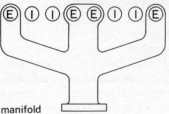

Fig. 4.7   Exhaust manifold

gases from another cylinder. This feature may be obtained by (a) having one pipe to each port, (b) so shaping the entries to the manifold that back feed cannot occur and (c) arranging pairs of ports to feed into one manifold entry.

A very common arrangement for four-cylinder engines has a separate entry bore from each of the end ports and a central entry bore from the paired central ports, all three bores joining just before the exhaust-pipe connection. A more efficient, but more bulky, manifold consists of pipes grouped in pairs which are then joined at a set distance from their flanges, i.e. pipes from ports one and four are joined, and pipes from ports two and three are joined. The resulting pair of larger pipes are then joined just before the exhaust pipe connection. This type of manifold uses the gas pulsations of one cylinder's scavenging to assist the scavenge of its paired cylinder, the pipe lengths determining the engine speed at which this assistance is greatest.

Six-cylinder manifolds may be made as one manifold serving all six exhaust ports, or as two manifolds serving groups of three ports. In the latter arrangement the two collecting pipes may be joined into one pipe or joined to their own silencing system.

EXHAUST SYSTEM

The system consists of a steel drop pipe (which is connected to the manifold), one or more silencers, a steel tail pipe, and the necessary mounting brackets. As modern engines are arranged in flexible rubber mountings, which permit a fair amount of engine movement relative to the chassis or sub-frame, the exhaust system must permit this movement without strain. At one time the drop pipe included a length of flexible steel tubing, and the silencer and tail pipe were rigidly attached to the frame. The flexible steel tubing had only a relatively short service life due to the effects of large variations in temperature, and corrosion, so the modern systems, particularly for commercial vehicles where greater engine movement occurs with greater chassis flexibility, are supported by two or more bonded rubber mountings. These may be of the cylindrical or sandwich type, and the drop pipe may be secured to the bell housing of the clutch by a rigid bracket. Some exhaust pipes and silencers may be protected from corrosion by special metallic-based paints, or by a metal spraying process.

Exhaust silencers

All motor vehicles intended for use on public roads must be fitted with efficient silencers. Each exhaust stroke emits a sound wave composed of higher and lower frequencies of compression vibration, the lower frequencies being due to resonance and the higher to the release of gases under high pressure. In modern engines the exhaust gas velocity will be in excess of 45 m/s, the temperature between 600° C and 850° C, and the ejection pressure between 200 kN/m² and 400 kN/m².

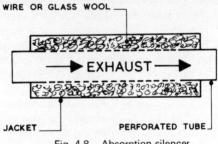

Fig. 4.8   Absorption silencer

The higher frequencies may be damped down by passing the gases through an absorption type of silencer in which a perforated steel tube is surrounded by glass or wire wool (see Fig. 4.8). The gases pass through the tube in an unobstructed flow, while the high frequency sound waves pass through the perforations to be damped down by the wool.

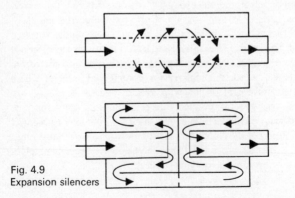

Fig. 4.9
Expansion silencers

The lower frequencies may be damped down by passing the gases through a silencer of the expansion or capacity type in which the gases are permitted a controlled expansion (see Fig. 4.9).

One type of silencer alone cannot damp down both ranges of sound waves, so silencers are employed as either two different units in one system or as one unit which combines both types, i.e. a composite silencer (see Fig. 4.10). The latter may be easier to fit to some vehicles. Composite silencers may be oval, circular, or rectangular in cross-section.

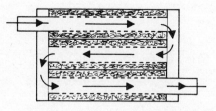

Fig. 4.10   Composite silencer

MULTI CARBURETTORS

The Volumetric Efficiency of an engine could apparently be increased by the use of larger bores in the intake manifold and a larger-diameter venturi in the carburettor. In practice this would result in very poor petrol atomization and inadequate suspension of the petrol drops in the air flowing through the manifold. The size of the venturi and jets is largely determined by the bore, stroke, and maximum speed of the engine, so the practical alternatives for increasing the Volumetric Efficiency lie in the use of multiple carburettors, and manifolding which provides a more direct path to the cylinders.

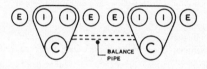

TWIN CARBURETTORS   GROUPED INLET PORTS

Fig. 4.11   Four-cylinder porting

Twin carburettor

A given engine will provide more power and have a better performance when fitted with two carburettors and a corresponding manifold. These carburettors will be identical and will have the same size of venturi and jets as the single carburettor they replace. Their throttle valves will be interconnected by a clamp link but their actions will have to be synchronized. A twin-carburettor assembly on a four-cylinder engine will normally provide more power, but the fuel consumption will be higher. On a six-cylinder engine the fuel consumption is not increased to the same extent.

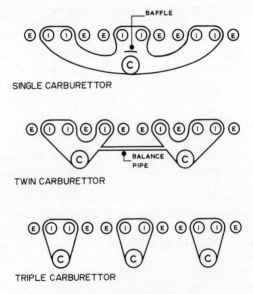

SINGLE CARBURETTOR

TWIN CARBURETTOR

TRIPLE CARBURETTOR

Fig. 4.12   Six-cylinder porting

Triple carburettor

Some six-cylinder engines are fitted with three carburettors but while these may look identical the centre one will require smaller main jets.

Dual carburettor

These have two venturi and jet systems built into one body. One venturi and jet system supplies the mixture for all normal running while the second comes into operation only for acceleration and full-power conditions. The function of the second system is to provide a greater volume of mixture at high speeds while maintaining good venturi and manifold action. The throttle valves are interconnected and must be set to the manufacturers' instructions.

Tuning multi carburettors

The ignition timing, sparking-plug and contact-breaker gaps, and valve clearances must be correct before carburettor tuning is carried out. Each carburettor is set up as a single unit, and the idling-speed stops are synchronized first. The throttle interconnecting clamp is released and the stops reset so they will just trap a thin piece of paper. The stops are then screwed in one complete turn and the engine started. The correct idling speed is then obtained by adjusting the stops *equally* – this being checked by listening to the intensity of the air hiss at each intake. If one is louder the stop must be unscrewed until the hiss is the same at each intake. A vacuum gauge may also be used to check speed synchronization.

The mixture strength adjustment is then altered, in turn, until a regular exhaust note is obtained. If the engine speed increases, both speed stops must be unscrewed by equal amounts until the correct idling speed is regained. An excessively weak mixture will be indicated by a splashy misfire in the exhaust note while a regular misfire, perhaps with black smoke, indicates an excessively rich mixture. When both of these adjustments give satisfactory results the throttle clamp is tightened, and the air cleaners replaced ready for the road test.

PETROL INJECTION

Carburettor disadvantages

Carburettor and manifold systems are relatively simple, effective, and cheap but they limit engine performance and fuel economy. The Volumetric Efficiency is reduced by the restriction due to the venturi and throttle valve; mixture velocity is reduced by direction changes in the manifold; and hot spotting reduces the weight of the mixture charge. The different cylinders receive neither the same weight nor the same strengths of mixture.

Injection advantages

In petrol-injection systems the air is drawn directly into the cylinders, and an accurately metered charge of atomized petrol is injected into the air just before it enters the port. Petrol injection has the following advantages over the carburettor system:

(1) Increased power – due to the greater weight of air induced.
(2) Reduced petrol consumption – due to the more accurate metering of the petrol to suit the weight of air entering the cylinders.
(3) Greater flexibility – due to the increased power at all speeds the engine can run slower and accelerate faster.
(4) Cleaner exhaust; due to the accurate metering of the petrol it is more completely burned, reducing the exhaust content of unburned hydrocarbons and of carbon monoxide.

The Lucas petrol-injection system (Figure 4.13)

The system consists of a petrol tank; a paper-element type of filter; an electrically driven, gear-type, petrol pump; a pressure relief valve; a combined distributor and mixture-control unit; and the injectors – one of which is fitted at each inlet port. Plastic pipes, with metal connections and nuts, are used to connect the units.

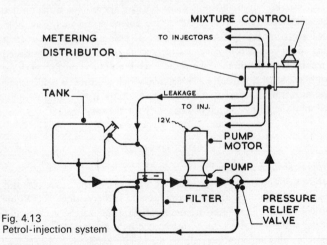

Fig. 4.13
Petrol-injection system

Filter (Figure 4.14)

This is similar to those used with C.I. engines but the filter elements are *not interchangeable*. Petrol passes through the element from top to bottom, the vee-shaped paper coils retaining the particles of dirt, and leaves the filter via the space around the centre bolt.

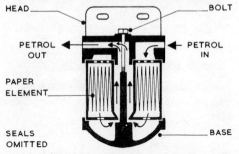

Fig. 4.14   Filter (seals omitted)

Pump

The pump is a twin-gear type with a nylon gauze filter in the intake port. It delivers petrol continuously at about $700 \, kN/m^2$ pressure at the rate of about 73 litre/hour. Petrol leakage from the pump is prevented by three sealing rings, and a shaft seal prevents petrol entering the motor. A tell-tale pipe in the motor bracket indicates when fuel has passed this seal.

The motor is arranged vertically above the pump and is a permanent-magnet type (cables must not be reversed). The motor drives the pump via a nylon coupling and requires 5 A at 12 V for its operation.

NOTE. The pump unit must always be replaced in its original position.

Pressure relief valve

This is fitted between the pump and the metering distributor to maintain the supply line pressure between 730 and $760 \, kN/m^2$. It may be adjusted by turning a screw, a quarter turn altering the pressure by about $35 \, kN/m^2$. Excess fuel is returned to the inlet side of the filter.

Metering distributor

The metering distributor delivers pressurized petrol to the injectors in the correct firing sequence. The mixture control determines, according to the load imposed upon the engine, the amount of petrol delivered. If either unit becomes faulty and has to be replaced the complete assembly must be recalibrated.

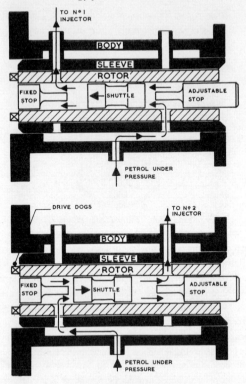

Fig. 4.15   Shuttle metering

The distributor is a shuttle metering device (see Fig. 4.15) in which a hollow, cylindrical rotor is driven at half engine speed. The rotor is enclosed by a cylindrical sleeve and itself encloses a cylindrical shuttle which has one fixed and one adjustable stop. The sleeve has inlet and outlet ports which coincide with ports in the rotor at different intervals of rotor rotation. The sleeve does not rotate and it is secured in a body which has one inlet port, and one outlet port for each injector and cylinder.

As the rotor turns, one of its ports coincides with an inlet port in the sleeve, and pressurized petrol passes into the centre bore of the

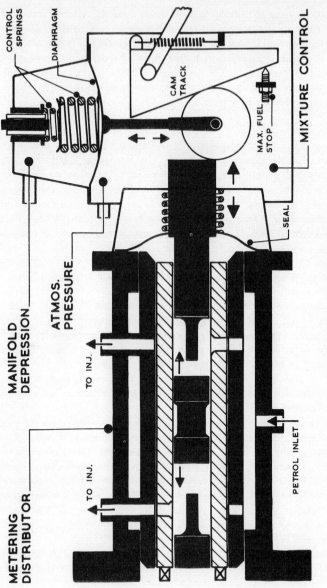

CONTROL SPRINGS

DIAPHRAGM

CAM TRACK

MIXTURE CONTROL

MAX. FUEL STOP

MANIFOLD DEPRESSION

ATMOS. PRESSURE

TO INJ.

SEAL

PETROL INLET

METERING DISTRIBUTOR

TO INJ.

Fig. 4.16 Combined unit

rotor to force the shuttle against one of its stops. After a further 60°
of rotor rotation (for a six-cylinder engine) pressurized petrol again
enters the centre bore – forcing the shuttle back to its opposite stop
and expelling the previous charge of petrol through the now-opened
ports to the injector. The combination of rotor rotation and shuttle
movement results in the delivery of pressurized petrol to the injectors
in the correct firing sequence.

Mixture control
This device alters the position of the adjustable (control) stop of the
shuttle in the metering distributor – so altering the length of shuttle
travel and therefore the volume of petrol delivered to the injectors.
The mixture-control device makes the petrol delivery sensitive to the
loading of the engine. A flexible diaphragm is influenced by manifold
depression and spring force, and its centre is connected by two links
to a cam follower. The follower contacts the control stop at one side
and a wedge-shaped cam at the other side.

When manifold depression is high (idling speed) the diaphragm is
deflected, against the spring force, by the pressure difference between
its opposite sides. The cam follower is drawn up the cam and is forced
towards the control stop, so forcing it inward and producing the minimum shuttle travel – and therefore the minimum petrol delivery.

As the engine speed is increased the manifold depression is reduced.
The deflection of the diaphragm is reduced and the cam follower is
forced down the cam. As the control stop is subject to the pressure of
the petrol it can now move outward until the follower is hard up against
the cam. The distance of shuttle travel is increased and so is the volume
of petrol delivered to the injectors.

An excess-fuel device is incorporated which permits much larger
deliveries to be made for cold-starting conditions. This device is
operated by the choke control and moves the cam away from its
normal maximum-delivery stop. This allows the control stop to be
forced farther out and so increases the travel of the shuttle. This device
is interlinked with the throttles to provide more air for fast, cold,
idling.

Injector (Figure 4.17)
The injectors are fitted in the inlet manifold near the inlet ports and
are of the simple poppet-valve type. A central valve is held closed by

a spring until the pressure of the petrol exceeds $345 \, kN/m^2$. At this point the valve opens outward and atomized petrol is sprayed into the air rushing through the inlet port.

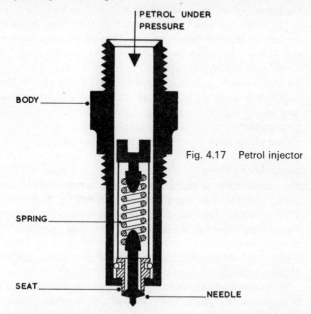

Fig. 4.17   Petrol injector

No adjustments are possible and the injector should be replaced if the valve sticks open. The most likely fault is dirt on the valve seat and this may be removed by blowing dry, filtered air through the injector at a pressure of about $550 \, kN/m^2$.

SUPERCHARGING

A given design of engine produces its maximum power when it causes the greatest expansion of the weight of air induced. Increased power can then only be obtained by (a) increasing the expansion of the normal air charge or (b) increasing the weight of the air charge.

Increased expansion
This implies the extra heating of the air charge and this can be obtained

by either burning more fuel or increasing the compression ratio. The need for fuel economy, complete combustion, and reduced air pollution rule out the burning of more fuel, so the alternative of increasing the compression ratio is adopted.

The extent to which the compression ratio may be increased is limited by the fact that maximum cylinder pressures increase at a greater rate than mean pressures. As maximum pressure determines the strength and weight of the engine components, and mean pressures the power output, a point is reached where the extra power obtainable is lost in rotating the necessarily stronger and heavier components. The use of higher compression ratios also increases the operating temperatures (hence pressurized cooling systems) and makes essential the use of the more expensive higher-octane petrols.

Increased weight of air
The weight of the air charge induced by a normal engine depends to a large extent upon the small pressure difference between the air inside the cylinder and the atmospheric pressure outside the cylinder. When the pressure difference is increased by increasing the pressure outside the cylinder a greater weight of air can be heated and expanded by the same weight of fuel, i.e. the engine is pressure or supercharged instead of being normally aspirated.

With supercharging, the maximum cylinder pressures do not increase at a greater rate than mean pressures and so greater power can be obtained without excessive maximum pressures. Cylinder temperatures are lower than when high compression ratios are used, and higher octane fuels are not so essential. A supercharger would probably be incorporated into the original design of a very high-performance petrol engine for a race or sports car but, as absolute power is not required, most car engines employ moderately high compression ratios instead of superchargers.

Although two-stroke C.I. engines must be supercharged, the supercharger can be applied to the four-stroke types with great advantage. The higher cylinder temperatures and pressures reduce the delay period of combustion and so provide smoother running. Increased torque is available at lower speeds. The same basic engine can, by varying the degree of supercharge, be made with different power outputs, and vehicles operating at altitudes where the air density is reduced can be supercharged to maintain their sea-level power output.

Types of supercharger

Superchargers may be considered as mechanically driven types or exhaust-driven types (turbochargers).

Mechanically driven

Possibly the most popular of these is the Roots blower (see Fig. 4.18) which is widely used with two-stroke C.I. engines. This type consists

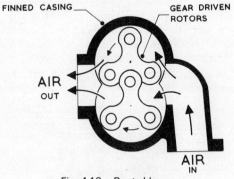

Fig. 4.18   Roots blower

of two figure-eight-shaped rotors which always maintain line contact. The rotors are gear driven, mounted on ball and roller bearings, and are enclosed by a heavily finned aluminium-alloy casing. This type will deliver $1.7\ m^3$ or air per minute at a boost pressure of about $35\ kN/m^2$, i.e. $35\ kN/m^2$ above atmospheric pressure when operating at 3000 rev/min. A larger, three-lobed, type has better sealing and a

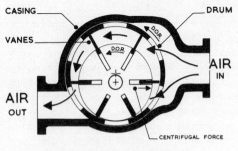

Fig. 4.19   Vane-and-drum type

more uniform delivery pressure. These types absorb between 5% and 10% of the power output and provide between 30% and 40% more power.

Eccentric vane types, such as the Cozette and the Powerplus, and centrifugal impeller types are also in service, but generally the mechanically driven types are being replaced by the various designs and capacities of the more efficient turbochargers.

Turbochargers (Figure 4.20)

In basic form the turbocharger consists of an exhaust-driven turbine which drives the impeller of a centrifugal blower – which in turn delivers an excess of air to the engine cylinders. The turbines of the larger units are axial-flow types, while those of the smaller units are radial-flow types, the latter being simpler to manufacture yet of high efficiency.

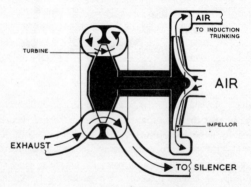

Fig. 4.20   Turbocharger

Turbochargers are high-efficiency units and cause only a very slight increase in back pressure. Their use results in a lower specific fuel consumption and they match engine demands very closely at all speeds. In some installations there may be a puff of exhaust smoke when the engine is accelerated. This is due to a small time lag between the injection of the extra fuel and the increased energy being available in the exhaust gas to speed up the compressor. This can, if the smoke is excessive, be overcome by the use of a device which makes the injectors depend partially upon the speed of the turbocharger.

Turbochargers, according to type and installation, operate at speeds

of between 24000 rev/min and 85000 rev/min. Their plain bearings
may be pressure lubricated from the engine system. Balance is of vital
importance at these speeds, and dirt must be excluded by the use of
properly designed, positioned, and maintained air cleaners. The compressor unit must be cleaned at regular intervals, and the whole unit
cleaned when the engine is overhauled.

Some turbocharging systems incorporate air coolers. These may be
water cooled and they permit lower engine air-intake temperatures –
so reducing the temperature of the exhaust gas (maximum 650° C) and
its effect upon the turbine. Other systems may employ a by-pass valve
near the turbine. This is controlled by the air-intake pressure and is
used to maintain the pressure ratio over a wide range of engine speeds
– so providing higher torque at low speeds and faster acceleration.

5

The Power Unit

The rotor (Wankel) type of engine operates on the four-stroke cycle in the same manner as the conventional spark-ignition engine, but it is free of the mechanical complication and losses associated with recipro-cating piston mechanisms, i.e. rotary motion is obtained directly from the expansion of the air charges. In the Ro.80 engine two rotors and main combustion chambers are used, the compression ratio being about 9:1 and the equivalent swept volume being $0.19\,m^3$. The com-bustion chambers are water cooled and the rotors are internally cooled by the lubricating oil. Dual-coil ignition is used and the spark plugs operate simultaneously. Two two-stage carburettors are fitted. The maximum torque is about 165 N.m at 4500 rev/min.

Construction (Figure 5.1)
The main combustion chambers are epitrochoidal in shape (very approximately oval) and the straight output shaft passes through their centres to drive the impeller of a three-stage hydraulic torque con-verter. The inlet and exhaust ports are at the same side of the main combustion chambers.

The rotors are shaped like triangles with curved sides and each side contains a cavity in which combustion is initiated. Spring-loaded steel strips seal the rotors to the walls and sides of the main chambers, there being in effect three combustion chambers in each main chamber. The spark plugs are opposite the inlet ports.

Operation
Induction. In Fig. 5.1 the chamber AB, formed between the main chamber walls and the rotor corners (apices) A and B, is at its minimum volume. As the rotor is turned anticlockwise the volume is increased, and the resulting pressure difference forces the mixture of petrol and

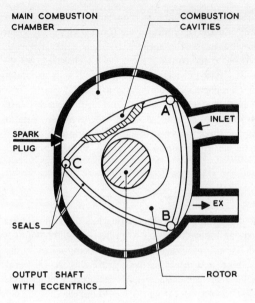

MAIN COMBUSTION CHAMBER

COMBUSTION CAVITIES

INLET

SPARK PLUG

SEALS

OUTPUT SHAFT WITH ECCENTRICS

ROTOR

EX

Fig. 5.1   Rotor engine

air to flow from the carburettor to fill the chamber. As corner B passes the upper side of the inlet port the induction operation for this chamber is completed – and that for the following BC chamber commences.

Compression. The continued turning of the rotor results in the volume of chamber AB being reduced and in the mixture being compressed into about one-ninth of its original volume. At the same time chamber BC is nearing the completion of its induction operation.

Power. As the centre of the side A–B of the rotor passes the two spark plugs the compressed mixture is ignited, and the resulting expansion forces the rotor to turn and rotate the output shaft via the shaft eccentric. While the bases are burning and expanding in chamber AB the induction operation of chamber BC is completed and its compression operation is commenced.

Exhaust. As the rotor turns anticlockwise under the pressure of the expanding gases the corner A eventually opens the exhaust port and the gases begin to leave the chamber under their own pressure. Further rotation reduces the volume of the chamber, the remaining gases are forced out, and the operating cycle for this chamber is started again as the corner B passes the upper edge of the exhaust port. During the expansion and exhausting of the gases in chamber AB the gases in chamber BC have been ignited and have begun expanding. At the same time chamber CA has almost completed its induction operation. The sequence of operation of the four-stroke cycle is carried out in each chamber in turn and, in effect, one complete rotation of each rotor supplies three power strokes to the output shaft. The shaft can therefore be said to be almost continually delivering power.

THE GAS TURBINE ENGINE

In recent years the gas turbine engine has been the subject of much experiment and development. Completely reliable units have been produced for automotive purposes but their fuel economy has been relatively poor, and attempts to improve this by the use of heat exchangers have not generally been commercially practicable as far as car installations are concerned. It would appear that the conventional spark-ignition engine will continue to be the power unit for cars for many years yet – in spite of its many inefficiencies. In the commercial-vehicle field, however, the gas turbine can compete now with the larger C.I. engines – and it may well eventually replace them for both rail and road purposes.

Leyland 350/400 gas turbine

This is the power unit for the Leyland 38 tonne six-wheeled tractor/trailer unit designed to operate at speeds of about 112 km/h. It is smaller and lighter in weight than a comparable C.I. engine, is much quieter in operation, and vibration is much less. Its service life between overhauls is much longer (about 800 000 km) and maintenance costs are about half. The fuel economy is comparable and the turbine engine can operate on any distillate fuel. The continuous use of leaded petrol, or diesel fuel having a content of more than 1% of sulphur, should be avoided, however, as this will reduce the service life. Atmospheric pollution by the exhaust gases is much less than with other types of engine.

The turbine engine is exceptionally smooth running and flexible,

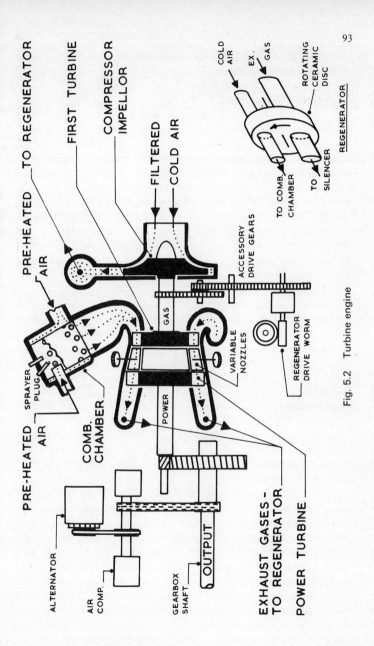

COLD AIR

EX. GAS

ROTATING CERAMIC DISC

TO COMB. CHAMBER

TO SILENCER

REGENERATOR

PRE-HEATED TO REGENERATOR

FIRST TURBINE

COMPRESSOR IMPELLOR

FILTERED COLD AIR

PRE-HEATED AIR

SPRAYER PLUG

COMB. CHAMBER

GAS

ACCESSORY DRIVE GEARS

VARIABLE NOZZLES

REGENERATOR DRIVE WORM

POWER

ALTERNATOR

AIR COMP.

GEARBOX SHAFT

OUTPUT

EXHAUST GASES - TO REGENERATOR

POWER TURBINE

Fig. 5.2   Turbine engine

and a five-speed, fully automatic gearbox meets all the requirements of both town and motorway driving conditions.

Construction (Figure 5.2)

The engine consists of two large main assemblies. These are the gas generator or gasifier assembly, and the power assembly. Each assembly is arranged around its own shaft and the two shafts rotate about the same axis. In the gas-generator assembly the impeller of a single-stage, centrifugal, air compressor is mounted on the front end of the shaft while the first or compressor turbine is mounted at the inner end. The second or power turbine is mounted on the inner end of the power assembly shaft opposite the compressor turbine, and a small gear at the rear end of the power shaft drives a much larger reduction gear attached to the input shaft of the gearbox. A large combustion chamber with a fuel sprayer and an igniter is arranged above the turbines. Rotating glass-ceramic disc-type regenerators (heat exchangers) are fitted at each side of the engine.

The gas generator shaft drives a train of gears which in turn drive the engine fuel and oil pumps, the regenerator discs, and the auxiliary pumps. The starter motor is geared to the shaft of the oil pump. The power turbine shaft drives the governor for the power turbine, the vehicle air compressor, and the alternator.

Operation

When the gas generator shaft is rotated at a fairly high speed, air, after passing through paper filters, is drawn into the centre of the compressor impeller. The air is then thrown off the edges of the rotating impeller vanes by centrifugal force and is directed into the combustion chamber, via the regenerator, by ducts in the engine casing. The pressure ratio is about 4:1.

In the combustion chamber the air is mixed with the burning fuel and its temperature is raised to over 1000° C. The rapidly expanding gases are then directed through the first turbine, where some of their pressure and heat energy is converted into mechanical energy which is used to drive the impeller of the air compressor. The gases then pass through variable nozzles to the second or power turbine where their remaining pressure energy is converted into mechanical energy which is used to drive the gearbox and final-drive units.

The gases leaving the power turbine still possess a considerable amount of heat energy. Before passing into the exhaust system a great deal of this heat is removed by passing the gases through the slowly rotating regenerator discs. These discs then heat the compressed air as it is passed through them before entering the combustion chamber. A considerable reduction in fuel consumption is obtained as a result of heating the air before combustion.

Starting

A normal 24 V starter motor is used to rotate the gas-generator shaft and this drives the fuel pump. At the same time a solenoid-controlled fuel valve is opened and a small, electrically driven, air pump provides an immediate supply of air to atomize the fuel. The fuel/air mixture is then ignited by an electric spark from the igniter plug. Once it has started, combustion is continuous, and the expansion of the gases results in the first turbine and the impeller of the compressor being driven at rapidly increasing speeds. When about one-quarter of the normal running speed (19 000 rev/min) is reached, a pressure switch disconnects the starter motor, the air pump and the igniter, and the gas-generator assembly accelerates up to half speed – this being the idling position set by the fuel-pump governor.

The speed of the engine is controlled by the accelerator pedal which alters the setting of the fuel-pump governor. It also (in conjunction with speed and temperature signals from the engine) controls the variable nozzles of the power turbine, i.e. determines the angle at which the gases strike the power turbine blades. At gas-generator idling speed the nozzle is in its mid position. The closing of the nozzle in the forward direction provides the power transmission position; closing the nozzle in the reverse direction provides engine braking.

Cylinder bore wear

Causes of wear

Wear of cylinder bore, piston, and piston ring can be attributed to three factors:

(a) Abrasion – the abrasive action of dust particles and carbon, the dust being carried by the air consumed by the engine and the carbon being the product of the combustion of both fuel and lubricating oil. Abrasion accounts for the greater part of wear of these components, and it may be greatly reduced by the use of correctly designed, fitted, and maintained air cleaners.

(b) Corrosion – during combustion. The thin film of corrosion left after each power stroke is scraped away by the piston rings, and tends to form sludge in the engine oil. Corrosion may be reduced slightly by the regular use of good-quality oils and fuels.

(c) Friction. The remaining small proportion of wear occurs as the result of friction between the moving surfaces, and may be reduced by the use of the correct lubricants.

Reduction of wear

The amount of wear taking place over a given period of use (miles or kilometres) can be reduced by attention to:

(1) The use of nitrided or hardened alloy steel or iron liners.
(2) The use of chromium-plated upper-cylinder walls.
(3) The use of colloidal-graphite upper-cylinder lubricants.
(4) The use of well designed pistons and rings which reduce the quantity of exhaust gas entering the sump (blow-by).
(5) A good sump-ventilating system which reduces the volume of blow-by gas dissolved by the oil – and so reduces the acids formed.
(6) A quick warming of the engine from cold (fast idle) and maintaining the engine at its normal operating temperature.

Position of wear

Cylinder wear does not occur evenly over the surface area of the bore (see Fig. 5.3). The greatest amount of wear takes place at the thrust side where the top piston ring travels, i.e. where the piston exerts the greatest force on the connecting rod and the greatest side thrust on the

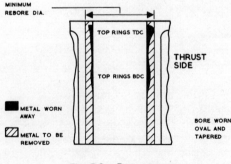

Fig. 5.3   Bore wear

bore. Wear also occurs at the lower ring position but to a lesser degree. Cylinder bores therefore wear both oval and tapered. Note that the most rapid *rate* of wear takes place during the running-in period. Fine finishes are therefore essential.

Measurement of wear

It is common practice to regard cylinder wear as the difference between the *original* size of the bore and the *maximum* size recorded by the cylinder bore gauge *in any position*. The original size is usually stamped upon the piston crown but the *unworn* portion of the top of the bore may be measured as a check. If the largest gauge reading occurs at the centre of the ring travel in the bore a tight piston or dirty oil should be suspected. A cylinder bore gauge should be used in preference to an internal micrometer as the latter is not easy to use accurately in deep bores. Six readings are usually taken, three in the thrust direction and three in the non-thrust direction, at top, centre, and bottom ring-travel positions and the maximum reading obtained compared with the original size.

Visual inspection

The bores should be visually inspected before any reconditioning work is begun, attention being paid:

(a) Deep scores. These will permit excessive exhaust gas blow-by and also result in an excessive oil consumption. Reboring or sleeving will be necessary.

(b) Dull, brown-coloured patches on the surface of the bore instead of a metallic polish. These' patches indicate hot spots or probable sleeve distortion. The water jackets must be cleared of baked sludge and/or a new sleeve must be fitted.

(c) Cracks. If these are small, and are not leaking water or gas pressure, a new sleeve may be fitted. If they are large the cylinder block must be replaced or be repaired by a specialist welding firm.

Reconditioning

Table 5.1 gives a general idea of the work which may be required as a result of the inspection of an engine main assembly.

Pistons are manufactured in oversizes, usually 0·020 in, 0·030 in, 0·040 in, and 0·060 in. (0·508 mm, 0·782 mm, 1·016 mm and 1·524 mm). These are awkward sizes which will disappear when design is carried

Table 5.1

Bore diameter	Maximum bore wear	Main and big-end condition	Work required
Up to 89 mm	Up to 0·127 mm	Within makers limits	Fit new standard rings
	Up to 0·1778 mm	Slightly outside limits	Fit new pistons with extra scraper rings. Remove unworn ridge at bore tops
		Well outside limits	As above, plus shaft and bearing replacement
	Over 0·254 mm	Within limits	Rebore or resleeve. Fit new shell bearings
	0·1778 mm to 0·381 mm	Slightly outside limits	Fit special steel rings (e.g. Duoflex, Cords, ApEx) and new shell bearings. Remove bore ridges
Over 89 mm	Up to 0·1778 mm	Within limits	Fit new standard rings
		Slightly outside limits	Fit new pistons with extra scraper rings. Remove bore ridge
		Well outside limits	As above, plus shaft and bearing replacement
	Over 0·381 mm	Within limits	Rebore or resleeve. Fit new shell bearings
	0·1778 mm to 0·381 mm	Slightly outside limits	Fit special steel rings and new shell bearings. Remove bore ridges

out in SI units. It is advisable to clean up the most-worn bore first with the boring bar, and to then obtain the nearest size of piston *above* the cleaned-up diameter. If oversize pistons are not available, the block must be sleeved back to standard size. One bore only of a multi-cylinder engine must not be bored oversize or engine balance will be destroyed.

Cylinder bore truing
Several methods are used for both producing and reconditioning cylinder bores.
(a) Boring. In which the cutting is done by a tool tipped with tungsten-

carbide, a very fine feed being employed. Fixed and portable machines are available.

(b) Grinding. This is usually a method for a factory or specialist firm as the machines are very expensive and need highly skilled operators. Grinding is a quick and accurate method, and it provides a very good finish.

(c) Honing (Fig. 5.4). In this method hones (rectangular lengths of grindstone material with a curved working face) are passed up and down the bore while being forced to contact the sides of the bore.

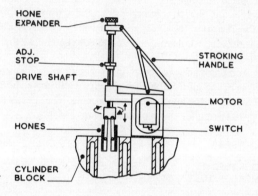

Fig. 5.4
Honing bar

One method is to hone finish a bore which has been made round and parallel by a boring bar. In this method the hones are fairly short and of a fine grit. The second method is usually a factory method in which very long and coarse grit hones are centred in the top and bottom of a cast bore to bring it to approximate size, fine hones being used to bring the bore to its finished size.

The boring bar (Figure 5.5)

Function

Boring bars are used to produce a cylindrical bore which is accurate in size to 0·01 mm, parallel, and round.

Construction

Portable boring bars consist of the following units:

(a) A rigid and heavy base which acts as a mounting for all the other units. This base has an accurately ground, flat, under-surface which is firmly clamped to the top of the cylinder block during the boring operation.

(b) A rigid and heavy cylindrical bar which can be raised or lowered in the bore by both hand and machine feed. This bar encloses and supports the drive shaft of the cutter although it does not itself rotate.

(c) A worm gearbox which is arranged at the upper end of the bar and which is driven by a grooved shaft which maintains the drive as the bar is fed through the bore. The cutter head is arranged at the lower end of the bar and has a slot and locating peg for the cutter. It also incorporates an expanding catspaw device which is used to centralize the whole machine to the bore before the final clamping to the cylinder block.

(d) An Acme-thread lead screw and engaging nut. The lead screw is driven by the motor attached to the base of the machine and feeds the bar down the bore as the cutter rotates. The electric motor has a stepped vee-pulley which provides a range of speeds.

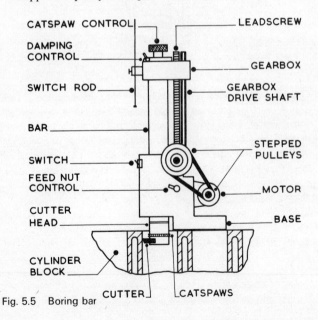

Fig. 5.5   Boring bar

(e) A motor-driven gearbox which drives the lead screw and the grooved shaft at preselected feeds and speeds – to suit the bore diameter and the depth of cut required.

(f) A control rod which is set to switch off the motor when the cutter clears the bottom of the bore.

Operation

(1) After removing the cylinder head studs, and filing down any portions of the head lifted during their removal, the cylinder block must be carefully cleaned and its top checked for flatness. It should also be checked for lying at right angles to the centre lines of the cylinder bores.

(2) The mounting face of the base of the boring bar must be cleaned and any burrs removed. The bar is then lightly clamped to the block in its approximate position, and the cutter bar hand wound down. The catspaws are then expanded to touch the bore, usually at the unworn top ridge but possibly at the bottom of the bore if this is well supported and free from distortion. The clamping device is then tightened and locked, and the switch control rod set. The catspaws of the Buma machine are then retracted (left expanded with the Van Norman machine).

(3) The necessary speeds and feeds are then selected after reference to the bore size and the manual of the machine.

(4) The cutter is sharpened on the motor-driven diamond/oil lap, the correct angles being obtained by the use of a sharpening jig. The cutting edges must be carefully examined for any signs of splintering, and the cutter is then fitted into its holder. The cutter and holder are fitted into a special size-setting micrometer. The micrometer is set to the size for the first roughing cut and the cutter is brought carefully *up to the micrometer anvil* by tapping it gently against its pin. Usually roughing cuts of up to 1·25 mm may be taken, but finishing cuts should not exceed about 0·125 mm.

(5) The cutter and its holder are then fitted into the cutter head, and are locked and located. Swarf-collecting devices may be fitted at the bottom of the bore. The bar is then lowered to the top of the bore, the motor is switched on, and the cutter rotates. When the feed nut is engaged with the lead screw the cutter is fed steadily through the bore. If the bore has slots for connecting-rod clearance at its lower end the bar will vibrate when the cutter reaches them. This

vibration may be counteracted by the use of a special damping device.

(6) As the cutter clears the bottom of the bore the control rod switches off the motor. The feed nut is then disengaged from the lead screw, and the bar hand-wound back to the top of the bore. The cutter is then removed and set to the size of the next cut – and the operation repeated until the finished size is obtained.

Crankshaft and bearing checking

Crankshaft

The main journals and crankpins of the crankshaft must be round, parallel, and free from scores and ridges. Correction methods include grinding, honing, and hand cutting. Where thin-wall, shell bearings are used, the journal or crankpin must be corrected by grinding because only a limited range of undersize shell bearings is available, i.e. the specified undersizes of pin must be adhered to. Where the older, thick-wall, white-metalled bearings are used, it is possible to bore and hand scrape a bearing to a non-standard pin.

Limits

Manufacturers' limits must always be adhered to, but generally a crankshaft must be reconditioned when wear has resulted in more than 0·075 mm of ovality on main journals and more than 0·05 mm on crankpins. Crankshafts must also be checked for bow (maximum 0·075 mm at their centre of length) and for cracks.

This type of work is usually carried out in specialist workshops because of the cost of the machines and the skilled labour required but it can be done by a skilled lathe operator if he has suitable grinding attachments available. Specialist workshops are also equipped with magnetic crack detectors.

Bearings

Main. The bearings must be replaced if they are deeply scored or if they show signs of the breaking up of their surfaces. They must also be replaced when the clearance exceeds between 0·125 mm to 0·175 mm. The rebuild clearance is usually between 0·025 mm and 0·05 mm.

Big-end. As for main bearings for limits and visual inspection.

Crankshaft end float. This is usually between 0·1 mm and 0·15 mm when the shaft is assembled in the crankcase. End float is controlled by shims attached to the housing of one main bearing.

Small ends. Where bushes are fitted, the gudgeon pin must be just a free fit but there must be no side movement.

NOTE. Always check big-end joint faces for evidence of filing. Thin-wall shell bearings are not adjustable but they must be checked for the correct nip – the nip is all that prevents their rotation, i.e. they are an interference fit in their housings.

The white-metalled, thick, shell bearings are sometimes adjusted by shims. These types must be carefully scraped to bed them to the journals or crankpins.

Fault Diagnosis

With the ever-increasing use of factory-made replacement parts and units, the modern motor mechanic has little need for a high level of skill as a bench fitter and machinist. The measure of his skill these days is his ability to locate faults both accurately and quickly, and to then rectify them in the minimum time possible.

The ability to diagnose faults quickly and accurately may, in a very few individuals, be a natural talent. For the rest of us this ability can only be developed through the combination of theoretical knowledge, practical experience, and familiarity or training with particular units. Quick fault diagnosis can be greatly assisted by the use of specially developed equipment and instruments – but success lies always in the following of a logical sequence of steps. These sequences can be memorized initially but eventually their use will become second nature, i.e. they will be used as a matter of everyday routine.

Without doubt the best form of maintenance is preventative maintenance – in which *regular* inspections and adjustments are carried out and in which faults are found and rectified *before* breakdowns and loss of vehicle-use occur.

As far as the power unit is concerned, the possible faults may be considered as falling into three main and different groups. These are:

(a) Mechanical – compression and timings, wear and fracture.

(b) Electrical – supply and ignition.

(c) Fuel – supply and carburation.

Mechanical faults can occur in all three groups as a result of wear, maladjustment, and fracture; a fault in one group can also affect the operation of units in the other groups.

The first task in engine-fault location is to determine in which group the fault lies. The symptoms, or warnings, of faulty operation will provide rough guidance, e.g. a complete and sudden engine stoppage is usually due to some electrical fault. A fuel supply or carburation fault usually makes itself known through misfiring, spitting back, and erratic running. Unless some part has fractured – and the resulting noise will indicate which – the complete stoppage of the engine is very seldom due to a mechanical fault. Mechanical faults usually result in a gradual fall off in performance and economy.

Always carry out a quick preliminary check of the following:

(1) Cylinder compressions. These must be approximately equal – check by means of (a) the starting handle or (b) a compression tester – with the throttle held open.
(2) Ignition. Check for a strong spark at each spark plug.
(3) Fuel. Check that petrol is reaching the float chamber of the carburettor.

The results of these preliminary checks, together with the known symptoms, should indicate the most probable area in which the fault will be located.

Table 5.2   Engine noises

Fault	Sound produced
Dry distributor cam	Continuous squeaking
Excessively worn generator armature and brushes	Continuous squeaking
Slack fan belt	Intermittent squeaking
Air leaks into the intake manifold	Whistle or hiss at higher engine speeds
Excessive tappet clearance	Continuous very light tapping
Excessively worn gudgeon pins	Regular light tapping at certain speeds
Excessively worn big-end bearings	Light to medium tapping
Excessively worn main bearings	Low rumble or thudding
Excessive crankshaft end float	Heavy intermittent thudding
Loose flywheel	Heavy intermittent thudding
Excessively worn pistons	Slapping noise which ceases as the engine warms up

OVERALL FAULT Starter-motor action Engine action	Mechanical faults	Electrical faults	Fuel-supply faults
DIFFICULTY IN STARTING Starter does not rotate crankshaft		Battery: discharged, connections slack, dirty or corroded Cable connections broken or slack Contacts of starter solenoid switch burned	
Engine does not fire		Starter motor: armature open or short-circuited, shaft bent or seized, field circuit open or short-circuited	
DIFFICULTY IN STARTING Starter rotates crankshaft slowly	Engine oil too viscous Engine too tight – not fully run in Water pump seized	Battery below half charge Terminals dirty or corroded	
Engine does not fire	Engine partly seized	Cable connections slack or dirty Contacts of solenoid switch burned Starter motor: partly seized, brushes dirty or excessively worn, armature shaft bent	

Table 5.3   Starting faults

Table 5.3 Starting faults

OVERALL FAULT Starter-motor action Engine action	Mechanical faults	Electrical faults	Fuel-supply faults
DIFFICULTY IN STARTING Starter rotates crankshaft at correct speed	Engine oil too viscous Incorrect valve clearances	Cable disconnected Condensation on HT of ignition system Spark plugs wet with petrol	Lift pump failure Carburettor controls set wrong for starting Sticking float needle – float action faulty Blocked carburettor jets
Engine does not fire	Incorrect valve timing Valve sticking or spring broken Exhaust system choked	Excessive spark-plug gap Excessive contact-breaker gap Retarded ignition timing	Air leaks into intake manifold Water in petrol
DIFFICULTY IN STARTING Starter rotates crankshaft at correct speed	Excessively worn pistons, rings, cylinder bores	Cable disconnected	Incorrect setting or adjustment of carburettor starting controls Petrol: not reaching the float chamber, not entering the manifold
Engine fires but will not keep running	Excessively worn valves, guides, seats Incorrect valve timing	Condensation: on HT of ignition system, in distributor cap Incorrect ignition timing Incorrect contact-breaker gap	Air leaks into the intake manifold

Fault	Mechanical causes	Electrical causes	Fuel-supply causes
POOR IDLING	Excessively worn cylinder bores, pistons, and rings Excessively worn valve assemblies Sticking valves Incorrect valve clearances Incorrect valve timing	Retarded ignition timing Excessive spark-plug gaps – defective insulators Cracked or wet HT cables Slack connections in ignition system – internal and external	Incorrect carburettor adjustment for speed and mixture strength Blocked idling jet Sticking piston (SU) Air leaks into manifold Choked manifold drain pipe Water in the petrol
LACK OF POWER, MISFIRING AND SPITTING BACK	As above Pre-ignition – need for decarbonizing and valve grind Exhaust system choked Brakes not releasing fully	Ignition timing retarded Advance mechanism seized or vacuum unit not working Plug heat range wrong Distributor unit – faulty condenser or connections – cap cracked or tracking	Petrol octane rating too low Blocked jets – weak mixtures Lift pump inadequate delivery Throttle valve not opening fully
RUNNING ON – when ignition is switched off	Burned exhaust valve Pre-ignition – need for decarbonization	Spark plugs of incorrect heat range	Petrol octane rating too low
OVERHEATING	Engine not fully run in Shortage of lubricating oil Water jackets partly blocked Radiator partly blocked – pump defective – thermostat defective – fan belt slack Brakes binding Clutch slipping Pressure cap defective	Ignition too far retarded Advance mechanism seized Vacuum unit not working Contact-breaker gap too small	Octane rating too low Excessive use of weak mixtures – jets too small

Table 5.4   Other faults

Speedometer checking

Road vehicles, by law, have to be fitted with a speedometer, and this instrument has to be maintained in good working order, drivers having to rely upon its accuracy to avoid the risk of prosecution for exceeding the legal speed limits. Most speedometers are accurate at about 50 km/h and read only slightly fast at about 65 km/h. At speeds beyond these the fast-reading error usually increases. Note that the error is not the same at all speeds. It is very difficult to carry out an accurate check of the speedometer reading at high speeds but it can be done with reasonable accuracy at speeds commonly used for legal limitation.

A workshop method of checking relies upon the fact that the mileage-recording part of the instrument (the odometer) is positively driven through a train of gears in the instrument – unlike the speed-indicating part which is driven via magnetic flux or centrifugal force. After first checking the drive cable and gear for smooth and easy operation, the vehicle should be driven, with as little speed variation as possible, over a distance known to be exact, i.e. taken from ordnance survey points and *not* milestones. Any error in the kilometre reading should be noted.

The vehicle should then be properly and safely supported with the driving road wheels clear of the ground. With the engine running, top or direct gear is selected, and the engine speed is set to give a steady speedometer reading of 48 km/h. A stop watch is started at the exact moment when a unit figure turns up on the odometer (distance recorder) and the watch is stopped at the exact moment when the next unit figure appears. Several time checks should be made and averaged. Any known distance error will be very small when only a distance of one kilometre is being checked.

At a constant speed of 48 km/h the time taken from one unit figure to the next should be two minutes. If this is so, then the speedometer reading is correct at this speed. If the time is *greater* than two minutes the speedometer is indicating a speed *greater* than the actual speed. If the time taken is *less* than two minutes the speedometer is indicating a speed *less* than the actual speed – and the driver may unknowingly exceed the speed limit. The check may be repeated at other legal limit speeds with a different standard time to check against. Excessively worn instruments will usually indicate a speed which is less than the actual speed, and these should be replaced if the error exceeds about 8 km/h. The main point is that the driver must be aware of the fact that he may be travelling faster than the instrument indicates at limitation speeds.

Note that the M.A.A. and the Weights and Measures inspectors strongly recommend that replacement speedometers are set to show the mileage recorded on the instrument they are replacing. This is to protect the mechanic and his employer from possible legal action under the Trade Description Acts.

Common speedometer and revolution counter (tachometer) faults may be diagnosed from Table 5.5.

Table 5.5   Speedometer faults

Fault	Causes	Remedies
Needle does not move	Drive cable or gear damaged	Replace
	Cable not engaging properly either end	Replace units as needed or refit correctly
	Gear teeth stripped inside instrument	Replace instrument
Erratic needle movement	Drive cable dry	Lubricate
	Worn or stretched drive cable	Replace
	Cable casing trapped, kinked, or bent too sharply	Fit correctly or replace
	Instrument faults	Replace
Needle steady but reading is inaccurate	Wrong size of road wheels or tyres	Recalibrate instrument (works or specialist repairer)
	Non-standard final-drive gears	
	Instrument faults	Replace
Noise (a) in cable	Cable dry or binding in casing	Lubricate, ease, or replace
(b) in instrument	Excessive wear or damaged parts	Replace

6

The Transmission

Simple train

Function

To increase the torque between two shafts rotating about a common axis. Power is the product of torque and speed ($P = T \times S$) and, if the power is constant at the driving shaft, a reduction of speed at the driven shaft produces an increase in torque at the driven shaft.

In epicyclic gearing systems the gears are all permanently in mesh, and there is no engaging of gears with, or releasing of gears from, the driven shaft when torque changes are required. Changes in torque at the output shaft are made, without interrupting the transmission of torque, by braking one element of the train.

Construction

The single epicyclic gear train consists of four elements. These are:

(1) The central gear or sun wheel (sun).
(2) Two, three, or four gears which are radially disposed around the sun wheel and are called planet wheels (planets).
(3) A planet-wheel carrier or arm which locates and supports the shafts upon which the planet wheels are mounted (carrier).
(4) An internally toothed ring gear known as the annulus. This meshes with and encloses the planet wheels.

The planet wheels are capable of three different actions. They may:

(a) Rotate upon their shafts but not move around the sun.
(b) Rotate upon their shafts and move around the sun.
(c) Move around the sun but not rotate upon their shafts.

How the planet wheels move at a particular moment depends upon which of the remaining three elements are driven, held stationary or braked, or left free to move. A single epicyclic train can produce four different effects at the output shaft if the sun wheel is driven, the planet

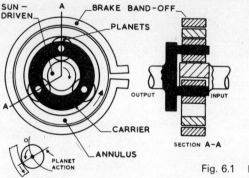

Fig. 6.1   Neutral

carrier is connected to the output shaft, and the annulus is fitted with an external contracting type of band brake.

Operation

Neutral (Principle 1). The sun is driven clockwise and the annulus is free to move. The planets are driven in an anticlockwise direction, rotating upon their shafts, but as the annulus is free they have no fulcrum from which to exert a leverage over their carrier. As the planets rotate they therefore remain stationary in relation to the sun, and exert no torque on their carrier and the connected output shaft. The annulus is forced to rotate slowly in an anticlockwise direction.

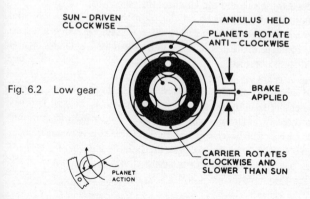

Fig. 6.2   Low gear

Low gear (Principle 2). The sun is driven clockwise and the annulus is held stationary by the application of the brake band. The planets are driven in an anticlockwise direction, rotating upon their shafts. As the braked annulus now provides a fulcrum the planets also move around the sun and exert a clockwise torque on their carrier and the connected output shaft. This action produces the greatest speed reduction and torque increase possible with this train. The change from neutral to low gear is made by applying the brake to the annulus – the driving shaft does not have to be released from the gear train.

Top or direct gear (Principle 3). The sun is driven clockwise, and the

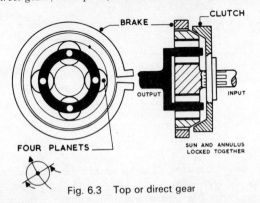

Fig. 6.3   Top or direct gear

annulus is driven at the same speed, and in the same direction, by means of a clutch which locks the two together. As there is no relative movement between the sun and the annulus, the planets cannot rotate upon their shafts. All four elements of the train therefore rotate with the sun and act as if the train was a solid coupling, i.e. when any two elements of the train are driven at the same speed the train locks up and a direct drive is obtained.

Intermediate gears (Principle 4). The greatest possible torque increase is obtained when the annulus is braked, and the lowest torque (direct drive) when the annulus is driven at the same speed as the sun. Torques between these two extremes can be obtained by the use of additional epicyclic trains, which drive the annulus of the first or main train at increasing speeds as they are brought into operation. The torque increases are reduced in corresponding stages as the speed of the output shaft is increased.

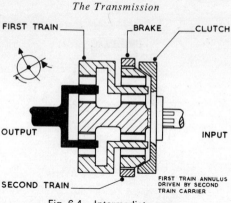

FIRST TRAIN BRAKE CLUTCH

OUTPUT INPUT

SECOND TRAIN FIRST TRAIN ANNULUS DRIVEN BY SECOND TRAIN CARRIER

Fig. 6.4 Intermediate gears

A reversing gear only (Principle 5). The driven shaft can be made to rotate in the reverse direction, and at increased torque and reduced speed, by connecting the annulus to the driven shaft, fitting the brake band to the carrier, and driving the sun. The sun is driven clockwise and

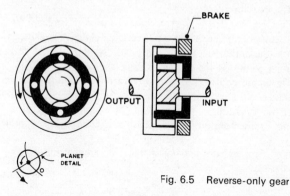

BRAKE

OUTPUT INPUT

PLANET DETAIL

Fig. 6.5 Reverse-only gear

the carrier is braked. The planet wheels are driven in an anticlockwise direction, rotating upon their stationary shafts and forcing the annulus and the connected output shaft to rotate in an anticlockwise direction at a reduced speed and with an increased torque.

Overdrive (Principle 6). The speed of the output shaft can be made greater than that of the input shaft by driving the carrier, braking the sun, and connecting the annulus to the output shaft. The carrier is

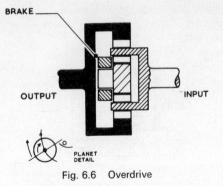

Fig. 6.6   Overdrive

driven clockwise and the sun is braked. The planets are forced to rotate upon their shafts in a clockwise direction and so exert a reduced clockwise torque, at a higher speed, upon the annulus and the connected output shaft.

The free wheel

The free wheel is a type of clutch which will transmit torque in one direction only, i.e. it is a unidirectional clutch. Free wheels were built into the output side of car gearboxes for a number of years and these units permitted the engine to drive the rear axle but not vice versa. The engine could not be used to retard the motion of the car but when road conditions were favourable the car could be coasted along with the engine operating at idling speed. This reduced the fuel consumption and engine wear, and it was possible to change gear without using the

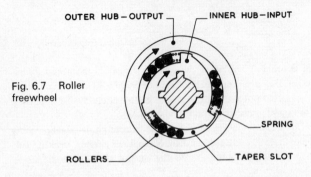

Fig. 6.7   Roller freewheel

main clutch. The device was put in and out of operation when required by the use of a dog clutch (engine driving or vehicle stationary).

In modern vehicles the unidirectional clutch is used as a part of more complicated units such as the overdrive, the torque convertor, and the automatic gearbox. The unidirectional clutch in one form consists essentially of an inner hub with tangential and tapered slots which house hardened steel rollers. The rollers are kept in alignment by a cage and are enclosed by an outer hub. The inner hub is usually driven, and the slight relative motion between this hub and the outer hub causes the rollers to move up towards the narrow end of their tapered slots. This movement results in a powerful wedge action between the hubs which locks them together. The outer hub then transmits the torque. When the outer hub rotates at the higher speed the rollers move back towards the wider end of their slots, the wedge action ceases, and torque is no longer transmitted by the clutch – in either direction.

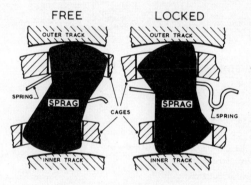

Fig. 6.8   Sprag freewheel

The overdrive

Function

To provide an extra high gear without increasing the complication of the gearbox, and without making additional gear changing necessary. When the overdrive is in operation the speed of the propeller shaft is greater than that of the engine crankshaft. Under favourable conditions this can lead to the use of higher cruising speeds, e.g. during motorway driving, or to a longer engine life and possibly 10% to 15% less consumption of fuel due to the lower operating speeds of the engine.

Construction (Figure 6.9)
The overdrive usually replaces the tailshaft extension and consists of the following units housed in an aluminium-alloy casting:

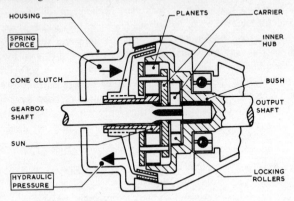

OVERDRIVE ENGAGED

Fig. 6.9   Overdrive (engaged)

(1) An epicyclic gear train.
(2) A cone clutch, with inner and outer linings, which is forced forward by the action of two hydraulic slave cylinders and to the rear by a set of strong springs.
(3) A unidirectional clutch.
(4) A high-pressure hydraulic system with its own sump, filter, pump, relief valve, and a high-pressure hydraulic accumulator and control valve.
(5) An electrically operated solenoid and control system which varies between different installations.

The output shaft of the gearbox is the input shaft of the overdrive unit, and it is splined into the inner hub of the unidirectional clutch fitted inside the annulus. A recess in the annulus acts as the outer hub and the annulus is integral with the output shaft. The carrier of the epicyclic train is also splined to the input shaft. The sun wheel is free to move on the input shaft and has a splined extension upon which the hub of the cone clutch can slide. The inner linings of the clutch contact the outer conical face of the annulus in direct drive, and the outer linings contact a steel face set in the housing in overdrive.

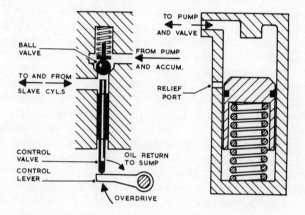

Fig. 6.10   Control valve (*left*) and pressure accumulator

The hydraulic pump is of the plunger type and is operated by an eccentric on the input shaft. The hydraulic accumulator is a cylinder containing a spring-loaded piston, the high-pressure oil delivered by the pump passing through a control valve and forcing the piston back against the force of the springs. A pressure of about $500 \, kN/m^2$ is maintained by the relief valve. The control valve directs the oil from the accumulator to the slave cylinders, and from the slave cylinders back to the sump. See Fig. 6.10.

Operation
In direct drive. The input shaft drives the annulus and the output shaft at the same speed and torque as that of the gearbox output, i.e. provides a direct 1:1 ratio. When the vehicle tries to overrun the engine the unidirectional clutch will cease to transmit torque – and engine braking would not be possible. This disadvantage is overcome by the use of the cone clutch, the springs of which force the clutch to contact the annulus. In the epicyclic train therefore the sun and the annulus are

driven at the same speed and the train locks up to provide a direct drive via the carrier, i.e. overrun torque is taken by the cone clutch and it is possible to use the engine to retard the movement of the vehicle (Principle 3).

In overdrive. When overdrive is selected, the electrical control system operates the solenoid which moves the control lever and valve. The ball valve is opened to allow high-pressure oil to pass into the clutch slave cylinders, forcing their pistons to move outward and engage the clutch with the stationary steel face in the housing. During this movement the clutch springs are compressed, and the torque is transmitted by the unidirectional clutch. The locking of the clutch holds the sun wheel but the carrier is being driven by the input shaft. The planets are forced to roll around the sun and drive the annulus and the output shaft in the same direction as the input shaft, but with increased speed and reduced torque (Principle 6). If overrun occurs the gear train takes the reverse torque and maintains engine braking.

Return to direct drive. When the control lever is again operated, the valve allows the high-pressure oil to escape from the slave cylinders into the sump. Their pistons are forced inward by the expanding clutch springs, which also engage the clutch with the annulus. As the engagement occurs the train locks up again, the torque transmission being maintained by the unidirectional clutch from the moment the sun ceases to be held stationary.

Special points
(1) Engine braking is always available.
(2) Engagement and release is made by one switch – declutching and speed matching is not required.
(3) Automatic engagement and release can be provided by incorporating a centrifugal governor and relay control system – and a manual override control can be retained.

Maintenance
(1) Check the level of the oil at about 1600-km intervals. Use the same type and grade of oil as is used in the gearbox.
(2) Change the oil and clean the filter at the same intervals as those recommended for the gearbox.
(3) Take special precautions to prevent dirt entering the unit.

Table 6.1   Overdrive faults

Fault	Cause	Remedy
Non-engagement	Shortage of oil	Top up
	No pressure in the accumulator	Check pump and delivery valve
	Control valve not passing oil to slave cylinders	Set valve lever in correct place on valve
	Mechanical damage to springs or gears	Strip unit – replace or repair as necessary
Non-release (*Examine at once. Do not use reverse gear*)	Control valve not passing oil from slave cylinders back to sump.	Re-set or repair
	Valve dirty	Strip and clean. Refit
	Clutch sticking	Strip and clean
	Damaged components	Strip and rebuild, or replace unit
Slip in direct drive overrun	Worn or damaged clutch linings	Strip and replace
	Broken clutch springs	Strip and replace
	Dirt in control valve	Strip and clean
Clutch slip in overdrive	Insufficient oil in unit	Top up
	Worn or damaged linings	Strip and replace
	Low pressure in hydraulic accumulator	Strip, clean, check pump and all valves

Detailed fault location in a particular installation should be carried out in accordance with the instructions of the vehicle manufacturer.

THE EPICYCLIC GEARBOX

These usually have four forward speeds and reverse and are used in conjunction with a fluid flywheel. Apart from the casing there are three main assemblies:

(1) The running gear which consists of four, interlinked, epicyclic gear trains and a multi-plate clutch.
(2) The brake band mechanism.
(3) The selector mechanism.

The running gear (Figure 6.11)

Construction

Train arrangement. The input shaft is permanently connected to the driven member of the fluid flywheel, and to the suns of the first and

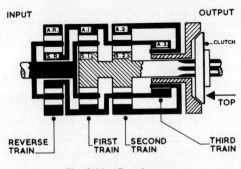

Fig. 6.11   Running gear

second trains. The third train is arranged between the second train and the multi-plate clutch, and the sun of the third train is free to move on the input shaft. The reverse train is at the output end of the gearbox and its sun is also free to move – but on the output shaft. Brake bands are fitted to the annulus of the reverse, first, and second trains, and to the sun of the third train.

Interconnections. The suns of trains 1 and 2 are driven clockwise when crankshaft torque is transmitted by the fluid flywheel. The planet carriers of the first and reverse trains are permanently connected to the output shaft. The first train annulus is permanently connected to the reverse sun, the carrier of the second train, and to the annulus of the third train. These components therefore always rotate at the same speed and under the same torque, and in the same direction, as the first train annulus. The sun of the third train is permanently connected to the driven member of the clutch.

Operation

NOTE. All trains operate through the first train and are used to increase the speed of the first train annulus in relation to its sun. The first and reverse train carriers, connected to the output shaft, always resist being driven, i.e. they will only rotate when the torque applied overcomes the drag due to the tyres, the final drive, and the resistance of the gearbox oil.

Neutral (All brake bands released). Sun 1 is engine-driven clockwise. As carrier 1 resists rotation, planets 1 are forced to rotate anticlockwise on their stationary shafts, so driving the annulus slowly in an anticlockwise direction. The movement of the free annulus prevents its use by the planets as a fulcrum from which they could exert a leverage over their carrier. No torque can therefore be transmitted by them to their carrier and the connected output shaft (Principle 1).

First gear (Annulus 1 braked). Sun 1 is engine-driven clockwise and forces planets 1 to rotate anticlockwise on their shafts. At the same time the planets are forced to roll around the sun and, by using the braked annulus as a fulcrum, apply a clockwise torque to their carrier and the output shaft. The carrier and the output shaft are driven at the lowest possible speed, and the highest possible torque, in relation to the input shaft (Principle 2).

Second gear (Annulus 2 braked). Sun 2 is engine-driven clockwise and forces its planets to rotate anticlockwise on their shafts. At the same time they are forced to roll around sun 2 and so apply a clockwise torque to carrier 2. Carrier 2 is connected to annulus 1 and in the first train both the sun and the annulus are driven clockwise – but at different speeds. The difference between the speeds causes planets 1 to rotate between their sun and annulus, and to drive carrier 1 and the output shaft at a higher speed but with less torque than in first gear (Principle 2 and Principle 4).

Third gear (Sun 3 braked). In the first and second gears, annulus 3 is driven clockwise by carrier 2 and annulus 1 but the third train does not take part in the drive. This is because sun 3 is free to move and therefore does not provide a fulcrum for its planets. When sun 3 is braked, planets 3 are forced to roll around their sun and exert a clockwise torque on carrier 3, and on annulus 2. In the second train both the sun and the annulus are driven clockwise at different speeds, and the difference causes planets 2 to rotate between them at a higher speed and under less torque than in second gear. As the speed of annulus 1 is increased the difference in speed between it and sun 1 is reduced and the output shaft is driven at a higher speed and with less torque than in second gear (Principle 4 used twice).

Top or direct gear (Clutch engaged). When the clutch is engaged, sun 3 is connected to the input shaft and is then driven clockwise at engine speed and torque. The speed increase through all the trains results in annulus 1 being driven at the same speed as sun 1 – and all the trains lock up to provide an output shaft speed and torque which is the same as the input (Principle 4 and Principle 3).

Reverse gear (Annulus R braked). In neutral the first and reverse train carriers are held stationary by the resistance of the output shaft. Sun 1 is engine-driven clockwise, rotating its planets anticlockwise upon their shafts and driving annulus 1 slowly anticlockwise. The reverse sun is free to rotate on the output shaft and, as it is permanently connected to annulus 1, it also is driven slowly anticlockwise. The clockwise rotation of planets R results in annulus R being driven slowly clockwise and not providing its planets with a fulcrum. When annulus R is braked it does provide a fulcrum and planets R exert an anticlockwise torque on their carrier and on the connected output shaft. In reverse gear the output speed is usually the lowest, and the torque the highest, provided by the gearbox.

NOTE. The oil pump for the lubrication of the gearbox is driven by the *input shaft*. The vehicle must not be towed for more than five kilometres or serious damage will result from shortage of oil at the gears and bearings. It is always safer to disconnect the propeller shaft or to tow with the rear end suspended.

The brake-band mechanism (Figure 6.12)

The brake-band assemblies each consist of inner and outer bands, each band carrying a hard-wearing friction lining designed to operate in oil. One end of the outer band is anchored to the base of the gearbox by the outer band hook and the other end is connected to the pull rod. The inner band ends are left free but the band is prevented from rotating by the inner band strut. The inner band is contracted by the contraction of the outer band. The anchorages of the bands are arranged at opposite sides to enable them to take the torque reaction forces when the bands are applied – relieving the shafts and bearings from these loads.

The pull rod passes through the thrust pad and the adjuster table, both being retained by a cylindrical adjuster nut which is located in a

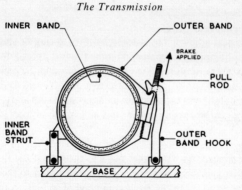

Fig. 6.12 Brake mechanism

recess in the adjuster table. The position of the adjuster nut on the pull rod determines the effective length of the pull rod. The pull rod is forced upward by the pivoting and lifting action of the thrust pad and this action may be brought about by spring force, by compressed air or vacuum servo pistons and cylinders, or by electrical solenoids.

Automatic band adjustment

It is most important that the correct clearance be maintained between the band linings and their drum. Each brake band is therefore automatically adjusted each time it is *released*.

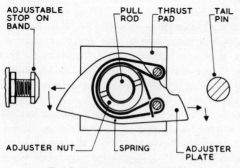

Fig. 6.13 Automatic adjuster

Construction (Figure 6.13)

The cylindrical adjuster nut is encircled by a spring of special shape. One end of the spring is secured to a pin attached to the adjuster plate. This plate can move in relation to both the nut and the adjuster table. The other end of the spring is secured to a pin attached to the adjuster table. The outer band is fitted with an adjustable stop and a stop pin is fitted to the gearbox casing on the other side of the adjuster.

Operation

(a) Band applied. As wear takes place at the linings the thrust pad is lifted higher, and this brings the adjuster plate closer to the adjustable stop on the band when the band is applied. The plate is turned anti-clockwise and the spring is forced to relax its grip upon the adjuster nut.

(b) Band released. As the band is released the adjuster plate moves slightly clockwise and enables the spring to grip the nut again. The further outward movement of the thrust pad forces the adjuster plate to contact the tail pin, and results in the plate and the spring being turned clockwise and tightening the adjuster nut. This reduces the effective length of the pull rod and so compensates for lining wear.

NOTE

(1) Gear slip may be corrected by operating the band of the slipping gear about twenty times.

(2) Fierce engagement may be corrected by slackening the adjuster nut of the band concerned by one turn, and then operating the band.

The selector mechanism (Figure 6.14)

The epicyclic gearboxes used in cars and buses became known as preselector gearboxes because the gear ratios could be selected in advance by the use of a small lever on the steering column, the actual change not taking place until a foot pedal had been fully depressed and then released.

The lever turned a camshaft in the gearbox which had a cam for each gear ratio which could be selected. Each thrust pad had a suspended strut which was forced outward (towards the side of the gearbox) by a spring-loaded plunger. A spring-loaded strut guide was arranged to force the strut inward at all times – except when prevented by the action of its cam. A bus bar, which extended the full length of the gearbox, was fitted below and inward of the lower ends of the struts and was very heavily spring loaded to tilt upwards at the strut side.

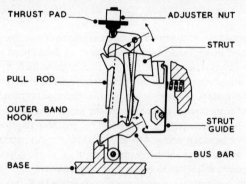

Fig. 6.14 Selector mechanism

When a gear ratio change was required, the movement of the lever turned the camshaft so its cams restrained the strut guide of the engaged strut and released the guide of the selected strut. The selected strut was forced inward by its guide until its tip contacted the side of the bus bar. When the pedal was fully depressed the bus bar was lowered and the spring was compressed. As the bar was lowered the strut of the released band was forced outward and away from the bar while the strut of the selected band was forced over the lip of the bar.

When the pedal was released the spring extended, lifting the lip side of the bus bar and the strut, pivoting and lifting the thrust pad, and pulling up the pull rod to apply the brake band – so bringing the selected ratio into operation. In the neutral position a neutral strut was engaged which held the bus bar in its lowered position. In top gear the top-gear strut turned the hub of the clutch through a helix action to engage the third gear sun to the input shaft, and so to lock up all the trains.

The preselector gearbox as used in cars has now been replaced by the fully automatic transmission system, and many buses and coaches are now fitted with semi-automatic transmissions in which the brake bands of the epicyclic gearboxes are operated by compressed-air servo cylinders. These may be controlled electrically (electropneumatic) or by air valves (pneumatic). In another system the operation and control is fully electrical, a rotary switch controlling the action of solenoids instead of air or vacuum cylinders.

THE SEMI-AUTOMATIC TRANSMISSION

A good example of a semi-automatic transmission is the pneumatic system used in Leyland buses and coaches. A four-speed and reverse epicyclic gearbox is used in conjunction with a fluid flywheel, the various ratios being brought into action through the use of compressed-air servo cylinders. An engine-driven air compressor provides sufficient volume and pressure of air to operate the brakes and the gearbox, and possibly servo cylinders for doors. The gearbox requires air at a pressure of between about 410 and 450 kN/m² . An excessively high pressure will result in the fierce engagement of all the gears while, too low a pressure will result in slip in the lower gears.

The driver's control is a small and gated lever which operates control valves which direct compressed air to the air cylinders arranged in the base of the gearbox. The gearbox can be locked in the neutral position by lifting the lever and turning it through 180 °. Reverse gear can only be obtained by lifting a shouldered sleeve below the gear-lever knob. In many of these transmissions a hill-holding device is incorporated in the gearbox. This device is a form of free wheel which operates when any forward gear is selected, its operation preventing the vehicle rolling backward on a gradient even when the engine is idling and the brakes are released.

Construction (Figure 6.15)

The band mechanism is basically the same as that already described, except for the addition of a spring-loaded device which ensures that the band linings are centralized on their drum when they are not applied.

The air cylinder is arranged at the pull-rod side of the band and it contains a spring-loaded piston with two sealing rings. The inner side of the piston crown is concave and is contacted by the ball end of the piston rod. The other end of the rod is connected to an operating lever which carries a roller cam and which is pivoted at its outer end. The roller cam contacts the underside of the thrust pad fitted between the top of the outer band hook and the underside of the adjuster table. The table is held by the adjuster nut screwed on the upper end of the pull rod.

127

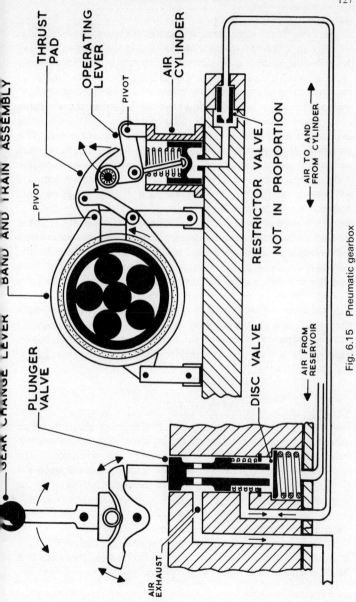

GEAR CHANGE LEVER — BAND AND TRAIN ASSEMBLY

THRUST PAD

OPERATING LEVER

PIVOT

AIR CYLINDER

PIVOT

BAND AND TRAIN ASSEMBLY

PLUNGER VALVE

PIVOT

RESTRICTOR VALVE. NOT IN PROPORTION

AIR TO AND FROM CYLINDER

DISC VALVE

AIR FROM RESERVOIR

AIR EXHAUST

Fig. 6.15   Pneumatic gearbox

Operation

Engagement. When a gear ratio is selected, the movement of the gear lever forces a hollow, spring-loaded, control-valve plunger to move down its bore in the control-valve block. The lower end of the plunger opens a spring-loaded disc valve which then allows compressed air to pass from the reservoir to the air cylinder – via a pipe line and a hollow, sliding restrictor valve. The pressure of the air forces the air piston upward and, through the action of the piston rod and the operating lever and its roller cam, forces the thrust pad upward and inward. This movement of the pad lifts the pull rod and so tightens the bands upon their drum. As the compressed air passes through the pipe connection at the cylinder end it forces the hollow restrictor valve to move inward and restrict the flow of air – so causing a slightly slower or more progressive application of the bands.

Release. When a different gear ratio is selected, the operation is repeated for the new band mechanism. As the gear lever is moved the control-valve plunger of the released band is lifted by its spring, and the disc valve is closed by its spring. The reservoir is therefore sealed off from the valve and the air in the cylinder escapes through the hollow valve plunger. The air piston is returned to the bottom of its bore, by the action of its spring and the toggle action of the thrust pad on the outer band hook, and the brake bands are released. As the air leaves the cylinder it forces the restrictor valve to move outward – so providing a larger escape port and a release action which is quicker than the application action.

THE FLUID FLYWHEEL

The fluid flywheel, or fluid coupling, is a form of clutch in which crankshaft torque is transmitted to the input shaft of the gearbox through the effect of centrifugal force upon a low-viscosity oil. The percentage of torque transmitted by the coupling depends upon the speed of the engine, i.e. the operation of the unit is controlled by the accelerator pedal.

Construction (Figure 6.16)

The fluid flywheel consists of two torus-shaped members which have flat and radially arranged vanes. The flywheel is deeply recessed and the driving member is bolted to it to form an oil-tight chamber. The

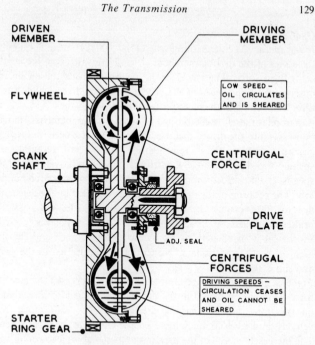

Fig. 6.16   Fluid flywheel

second and driven member is arranged inside the chamber, with its vanes opposing those of the driving member, and is bolted to the output shaft. The shaft is supported and located by opposed ball thrust bearings and passes through the driving member. A special design of adjustable or spring-loaded oil seal is fitted over the shaft at this point. The two members must never touch and are normally about 3 mm apart. The complete assembly is carefully balanced and the outer face of the driving member carries two screwed filler plugs. The oil level is determined by the upper plug when the two are arranged vertically.

In order to reduce oil turbulence and heat losses the driven member may have fewer vanes than the driving member, and an oil director ring may be incorporated. In some designs this director ring may be replaced by a baffle ring fitted at the centre of the driven member. This reduces its drag at very low engine speeds and so changes the slip characteristic slightly.

Operation

Idling speeds. At engine idling speed (500–600 rev/min) the oil between the vanes of the driving member is forced outward from the centre by centrifugal force. The shape of the member directs the oil on to the outer parts of the vanes of the driven member – from which it is then directed back on to the inner parts of the driving vanes. A slow circulation of oil is therefore established between the two members, and as the oil passes into the driven member its velocity is reduced and its kinetic energy is given to the driven member. The oil path resembles a coil spring formed into a circle. Centrifugal force is relatively low at idling speeds, and the velocity and kinetic energy of the oil are correspondingly low. The rotation of the driven member is opposed by the resistance or drag of the transmission, the weight of the vehicle, and possibly the brakes if applied. At these engine speeds the kinetic energy given up by the oil is insufficient to overcome this resistance and the driven member remains stationary. No torque is transmitted to the gearbox and slip is 100%.

Running speeds. As the speed of the engine is increased the centrifugal force acting upon the oil in the driven member is also increased. The oil therefore passes from the driving member with much greater velocity, and gives up much more kinetic energy at the driven member. The increased energy of the driven member enables it to rotate against its resistance and it begins to transmit torque to the gearbox. At engine speeds of between about 600 and 1000 rev/min the slip between the two members is reduced from 100% to about 15% and, as the engine speed is further increased, the slip is reduced to between 1% and 2%, i.e. the efficiency of the fluid flywheel at normal running speeds is about 98%. This high level of efficiency, combined with the very rapid and smooth reduction in slip (increase in torque transmission) is the main characteristic of this unit. It also reduces the shock of drive take-up and provides a much smoother or more regular torque at the transmission units. As the load on the driven member always results in it rotating at speeds less than those of the driving member – even at maximum speed – the circulation of the oil between the two members is always maintained. The transfer of kinetic energy is therefore always maintained and torque is transmitted to the gearbox.

NOTE

(1) According to engine speed, the fluid flywheel will transmit from

0% to 98% of the torque available at the crankshaft. It cannot increase the available torque under any circumstances.

(2) In spite of the 100% slip at low speeds there is always some drag on the driven member. An epicyclic gearbox must therefore be used in conjunction with this coupling instead of a sliding dog or synchromesh gearbox.

(3) The oil used in the unit must be non-corrosive and anti-oxident. It must be of low viscosity and high density. The use of an oil of high viscosity will increase the slip and reduce the efficiency.

THE HYDRAULIC TORQUE CONVERTER

Function

The gearbox is a mechanical torque converter, i.e. it changes the torque provided by the crankshaft by producing a change in its output shaft speed. The hydraulic torque converter does exactly the same job but with two very important differences. The torque changes resulting from the use of a gearbox progress in steps as each ratio is selected, the smoothness of the changes depending upon the skill of the driver. The accuracy with which the torque supplied matches that required also depends upon the skill of the driver. The hydraulic torque converter is capable of such an infinite number of combinations of speed and torque that it can match accurately, and automatically, every slight variation of load imposed upon the engine.

Construction (Figure 6.17)

The converter is similar in construction to the fluid flywheel but the differences are important. The operational difference is that the converter can multiply the torque provided by the crankshaft while the fluid flywheel cannot.

The converter consists of driving and driven members, and a reaction member or stator. One, two, or three stators may be employed. The driving member is called the pump or impeller and the driven member is known as the turbine. The impeller and the turbine face each other and the stator is arranged between them.

Impeller. The impeller is toroidal in shape and is mounted on the flywheel. The vanes are radially arranged and of aerofoil cross-section. They are also curved so that when centrifugal force causes oil to flow

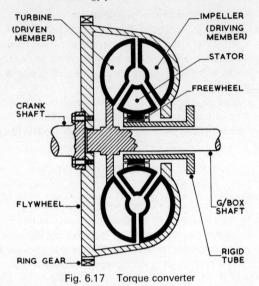

Fig. 6.17   Torque converter

along the vanes the oil is expelled with much greater velocity than is possible with the flat vanes of the fluid flywheel.

Turbine. This also is toroidal in shape with radially disposed vanes of aerofoil cross-section. These vanes are less in number than those of the impeller – to reduce oil turbulence – and their curvature is arranged to first lead in the direction of rotation and then to lead in the opposite direction as they near the centre of the turbine. The turbine is secured to the gearbox input shaft and is supported by opposed thrust bearings. It is completely independent of both the flywheel and the impeller, and is driven by the oil ejected from the impeller.

Stator. The stator is fitted into the oil path between the turbine and the impeller but mechanically it is independent of both. It consists of a set of vanes which are so curved that the oil leaving the turbine is redirected into the impeller in the direction of impeller rotation, i.e. the returning oil helps the rotation of the impeller instead of opposing it. The stator is mounted upon a unidirectional clutch or freewheel which is itself mounted upon a fixed tubular member. This clutch enables the stator to follow the impeller under certain conditions but never to move in the opposite direction.

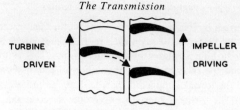

RETURNING OIL OPPOSES IMPELLER MOTION

Fig. 6.18   Action without a stator

Operation

Heavy-load conditions. Under these conditions, i.e. starting from rest, hill climbing or accelerating, the turbine is very heavily loaded and a torque higher than that of the crankshaft is required to cause it to rotate. The oil, due to centrifugal force and the curvature of the impeller vanes, is thrown out of the impeller at high speed. As it strikes the vanes of the stationary or slower-moving turbine its velocity is reduced and most of its kinetic energy is given to the turbine – causing it to rotate because a torque is being applied to it. As the oil then passes along the turbine vanes it is accelerated again by their curvature, its velocity and kinetic energy are increased, and it is directed into the stator vanes in a direction opposite from that of the rotation of the impeller. The angle

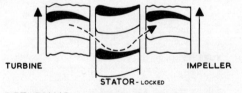

RETURNING OIL ASSISTS IMPELLER MOTION

Fig. 6.19   Torque multiplication

at which this returning oil strikes the stator vanes is such that the stator tries to rotate in the same direction. This rotation is prevented by the locking action of the unidirectional clutch, and the oil is therefore redirected by these fixed vanes into the impeller in the direction of impeller rotation. A further increase in velocity and kinetic energy occurs as the oil passes along the stator vanes and this energy is added to that imparted by the impeller vanes. The oil then leaves the impeller at even greater velocity and gives even more kinetic energy to the turbine, i.e. the turbine is rotated by a greater torque. The torque applied depends upon the relative speeds of rotation of the impeller and the turbine and the torque supplied is matched very accurately, and automatically, to the torque required to overcome the load against which the engine is working. In a three-element or single-stage converter there are three transfers of energy. Where more than one set of stator vanes are employed, more energy transfers occur. The torque multiplication of the converters used in automatic transmissions for cars is usually about $2\frac{1}{2}$, i.e. the converter multiplies the crankshaft torque by $2\frac{1}{2}$ when the turbine is held stationary. In other types of converter the torque multiplication may be as high as $6\frac{1}{2}$ to 1.

Light-load conditions. As the speed of the vehicle is increased, and the load on the turbine is reduced, the speed of the turbine increases progressively until it almost matches speed with the impeller. During the period of turbine acceleration the angle at which the oil leaving the impeller strikes the turbine vanes is altering, and less energy is given to the turbine, i.e. the torque acting upon the turbine is reducing. At the same time the oil leaving the turbine is striking the stator vanes at less acute angles, and the stator is therefore no longer locked by the unidirectional clutch. It now begins to rotate with the impeller and turbine.

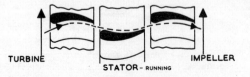

TURBINE   IMPELLER

STATOR – RUNNING

OIL RETURNS FREELY – TORQUE MULTIPLICATION CEASES

Fig. 6.20 Light-load conditions

Under these conditions the rotation of the stator provides a smooth return flow of oil from the turbine to the impeller, and torque multiplication ceases as the returning oil has little or no energy to add to the impeller. The smooth return action helps to reduce the very high energy losses due to turbulence and the production of heat. Under light load conditions about 90% of the available torque is transmitted. When the load on the turbine is increased its speed is reduced, and the direction of the returning oil is such that the stator is forced back and held stationary by the unidirectional clutch. Torque multiplication automatically occurs to suit the increased load – and continues until the stator is once again free to run with the impeller and turbine.

Advantages
(1) In common with the fluid flywheel, this coupling has a very smooth take-up of torque and it reduces shock loads on the transmission units and chassis.
(2) The torque changes are made very smoothly, and fewer changes are required when used in conjunction with an epicyclic gearbox.
(3) Within possible practical limits, the matching up of torque supplied to torque required is very accurate.
(4) Torque multiplication is provided automatically.
(5) Very little attention is required during its service life. (Many of these units are sealed during manufacture.)

Limitations
Theoretically the converter could be used to replace the clutch and gearbox. In vehicle practice, the converter is used in conjunction with two or more trains of epicyclic gears. This is because the converter, when multiplying torque by about 2, has an efficiency of only about 30%, i.e. the wastage of fuel is about 70%. Even when used with epicyclic trains the maximum efficiency is only about 90% – at top converter speeds. Most automatic transmissions employing a hydraulic torque converter therefore use the converter to modify the gear ratios and provide a smooth transmission and matching of torques.

Characteristics
The main characteristics of the torque converter are its efficiency and its torque multiplication, i.e. output torque divided by input torque. When the load on the turbine is so large that it cannot be moved the torque multiplication (stall torque) is at its maximum – but the efficiency of the unit is zero because a torque is being applied but no rotation is taking place i.e. output torque is zero. When the load on the turbine is so small that the turbine is rotating at almost the same speed as the impeller the torque multiplication is zero – the efficiency is also zero because the turbine, rotating with the impeller, has no torque acting upon it.

FULLY AUTOMATIC TRANSMISSION

In recent years fully automatic transmissions have been developed to suit the requirements of the smaller cars, and these units have replaced the various systems of two-pedal control in which the clutch operation only was automatic.

Advantages

The fully automatic transmission has the following advantages:

(1) Reduction of driver fatigue. This is a very important factor in relation to road safety and the use of these types of transmission enables the driver to concentrate on driving, the transmission automatically selecting and engaging the ratio most suited for each and every driving condition.

(2) Avoidance of clutch and gear mis-use. Automatic changing, plus the use of a fluid coupling, results in less transmission and tyre wear. Servicing is also reduced.

(3) Exact matching of torque supplied to torque required. The automatic transmission can do this far better than the average driver, and better than most experienced drivers.

(4) Great reduction of wheel spin under bad conditions e.g. ice, snow, mud, and sand. This reduction is due to the smoother take-up of drive and the more exact choice of gear ratio. These factors also assist in low speed manoeuvring.

Slight variations exist between different designs and applications but provision is usually made for a transmission brake, which is engaged when P (Parking) is selected, and for the starter motor to be inoperative except when P or N (Neutral) is selected.

The selection of L (Lock-up) results in manual control, i.e. the transmission will not change ratio automatically until such time as the driver has selected D (Drive). By depressing the accelerator pedal beyond its normal maximum position in top gear (kick-down) an immediate change to a lower gear can be obtained to provide acceleration for overtaking.

The Borg Warner 35 transmission

Construction (Figure 6.21)

The transmission is a self-contained unit which is bolted to the rear of the engine, replacing the conventional clutch and gearbox. It provides very smooth changes of ratio exactly suited to engine loadings, the speeds at which these changes occur being determined by the position of the accelerator pedal. The unit consists of:

(a) A hydraulic torque converter of the three-element, single-phase type. This provides an infinitely variable ratio between the limits of 2:1 and 1:1, and modifies the ratios of the gearbox. At a given moment the overall transmission ratio is the gear ratio multiplied by the ratio the converter is providing at that moment.

(b) An epicyclic gearbox which includes two metal, multi-plate clutches engaged by hydraulic pistons, two band brakes applied by hydraulic pistons, a freewheel or unidirectional clutch, and two epicyclic gear trains with helical involute teeth.

NOTE. The clutches and the brake bands are named according to their position in the unit and *not* according to their purpose. The sun wheels *are* named according to their purpose, i.e. forward and reverse speed suns.

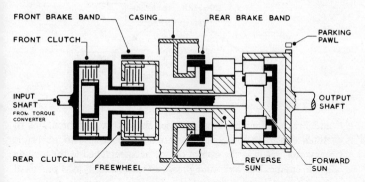

Fig. 6.21   Automatic transmission (neutral)

The arrangement of the trains is different from that in previous descriptions. Each train has its own sun but there is only one planet carrier and only one annulus. Pairs of planet wheels are used, the shorter and inner planets meshing with the forward sun and with the longer and outer planets. The longer and outer planets mesh with the reverse sun, and with the annulus which is integral with the output shaft. The forward end of the carrier is supported by a freewheel mounted upon a non-rotating centre support. The forward sun is connected to the front clutch and the reverse sun is connected to the rear clutch. The front band acts upon the drum of the rear clutch and the rear band acts upon the drum connected to the carrier.

(c) A hydraulic control system (Fig. 6.22) which is sensitive to the movements of (i) the accelerator pedal via a flexible cable (ii) the selector lever via a rod linkage and (iii) a centrifugal governor driven by the output shaft via hydraulic pressure. The operation and interaction of these three through a complex system of valves and ducts results in fluid under pressure being directed to the clutch

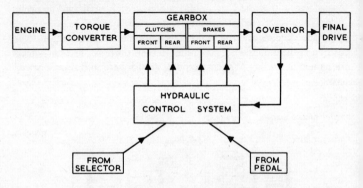

Fig. 6.22   Control system

and brake cylinders. This provides the correct combinations of clutch and brake engagement which, in conjunction with the torque converter, result in the output torque being matched to the loading of the engine. The hydraulic pressure is provided by two pumps of the internal/external gear type. The front pump is driven by the impeller of the torque converter and, when the engine is running at low speeds, provides fluid under pressure to charge the converter and meet the operational requirements of the gearbox. The rear pump is driven by the output shaft and meets all the fluid requirements when the speed of the vehicle exceeds 32 km/h. The two pumps operate in conjunction but the output of the front pump is reduced when the rear pump becomes fully effective. This enables the engine to be started via the transmission, i.e. tow starting is possible.

The detailed study of the layout and operation of the complete hydraulic circuit is beyond the scope of this book. It is suggested that interested students obtain copies of the manuals published by the various car manufacturers or, better still, attend the excellent courses arranged by them.

Mechanical operation

The selector lever on the steering column passes over a quadrant marked L, D, N, R, P. These letters give the lever positions for lock-up (no automatic changes), drive (fully automatic changes), neutral, reverse drive, and park. The starter motor can only be operated when P or N is selected, and the hand brake should always be applied.

Park (P). When P is selected the movement of the lever results in a pawl being engaged with the gear teeth on the *outside* of the gear-train

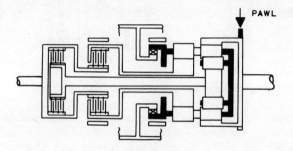

Fig. 6.23   Parking (*pawl engaged – output shaft locked*)

annulus. This action locks the output shaft and so provides a transmission brake which should always be engaged when the vehicle is to be left unattended, and when hand cranking, adjustment, and tuning operations are to be carried out on the engine. Note that P must never be selected when the vehicle is moving.

Neutral (N). When N is selected the clutches and the bands are all released, and no torque can be transmitted by the gearbox. The hand brake should be kept on until the vehicle has to be moved.

Drive (D). When D is selected the transmission will automatically change the gear ratios, and the output torques, according to the position of the accelerator pedal and the speed of the vehicle. This is the selector

position for all normal driving. An immediate change down, for overtaking acceleration, can be obtained by 'kick-down', i.e. pushing the
pedal past a detent, when the transmission will change into the next
lowest gear.

First gear (D). At low vehicle speeds with D selected the front clutch
is applied. This connects the turbine of the torque converter to the
forward sun gear, which is then driven in a clockwise direction. The
planets rotate on their shafts and tend to drive their carrier in an anticlockwise direction. This is prevented by the locking action of the

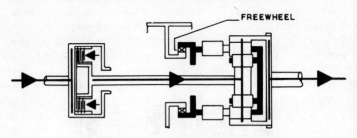

Fig. 6.24   Drive first
(front clutch engaged – freewheel locks carrier)

freewheel, and the carrier remains stationary. The planets drive the
annulus and the output shaft in a clockwise direction with less speed
and more torque than the crankshaft. The gear train provides a ratio
of 2·39: 1. This is multiplied by the torque converter so that at low
vehicle speeds the crankshaft torque is multiplied by all ratios between
4·78: 1 and 2·39: 1 – according to engine loading. When overrun
occurs, the freewheel releases the planet carrier and the gears run free,
i.e. there is no engine braking effect (see lock-up).

Second gear (D). As the speed of the vehicle increases, the hydraulic
control system operates to apply the front band in addition to the front
clutch. The front clutch connects the converter turbine to the forward
sun gear and the front band holds the reverse sun gear stationary. The
planets are forced to rotate on their shafts about the stationary reverse
sun and so drive the annulus and the output shaft in a clockwise
direction at a higher speed and with less torque than in first gear. The
combined gear trains provide a ratio of 1·45: 1 which is multiplied by
the converter ratios. At these increased vehicle speeds the crankshaft

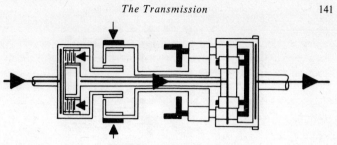

Fig. 6.25   Drive second
(*front clutch engaged – front band applied – reverse sun held*)

torque is increased by all ratios between 2·9:1 and 1·45:1, according to engine loading.

Third gear (D). As the speed of the vehicle is further increased, the hydraulic control system operates to release the front band and apply

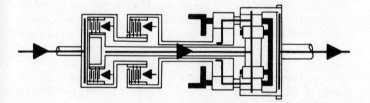

Fig. 6.26   Drive third
(*both clutches engaged – both suns driven at same speed – trains lock up to give direct drive*)

the rear clutch. The front clutch remains applied and the converter turbine is therefore connected to both sun gears. The gear trains lock up and rotate as a solid unit, providing a ratio of 1:1 which is modified by the converter ratios. At normal running speeds the crankshaft torque is multiplied by all ratios from 2:1 to 1:1, according to engine loading.

Lock-up (L). This applies to the first and second gears only and it may be selected to (a) provide engine braking or (b) to hold the transmission in either of the intermediate gears, i.e. it can override the hydraulic control system.

First gear (L). When L is selected at vehicle speeds of less than about

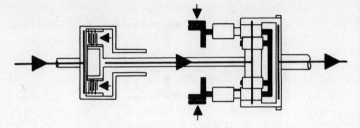

Fig. 6.27   Lock-up first
(*front clutch and rear band applied – engine braking possible*)

8 km/h, the control system operates to apply the rear band in addition
to the front clutch. The planets rotate on their shafts and drive the
annulus as in first-gear D but, as the carrier is braked instead of being
held by the freewheel, full engine braking is available on overrun.
The transmission will not change up until D is selected and the vehicle
is moving at a suitable speed. The ratios are the same as in first-gear D.
Second gear (L). When L is selected at vehicle speeds of over 8 km/h,
the control system operates to release the rear band and apply the front
band. This holds the reverse sun gear stationary and provides a degree
of engine braking through the gear trains. The transmission will not
change up until D is selected and the vehicle is moving at a suitable
speed. The ratios are the same as in second-gear D.
Reverse (R). When R is selected, the control system operates to apply
the rear clutch and the rear band. The rear band holds the planet

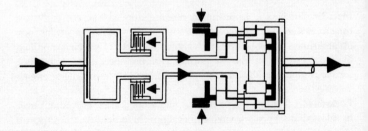

Fig. 6.28   Reverse
(*rear clutch and band applied – outer planet directions reversed*)

carrier stationary and the rear clutch connects the converter turbine to the reverse sun – driving it in a clockwise direction. The outer planets are driven in an anticlockwise direction and drive the annulus and output and output shaft in an anticlockwise direction at reduced speed and with increased torque. The gear ratio is 2·09:1 and this is modified by the converter ratios. The overall gearbox ratios in reverse are between 4·18:1 and 2·09:1, according to engine loading.

NOTE. All of the ratios quoted are modified by the ratio of the final drive unit.

Special points
(1) P and R must never be selected when the car is moving forward.
(2) D, L, and R must not be selected when the engine is running at high speed.
(3) Except in an emergency, L must not be selected at speeds above about 85 km/h.

Maintenance
The level of oil in the unit should be checked at about 4800-km intervals. The car should be on level ground and the unit at its normal running temperature. This temperature would be reached after about 8 km of driving. The engine should be run at idling speed for about two minutes with P selected, and the dip stick used to check the level while the engine is running. The dip stick should be wiped with paper or a non-fluffy rag, and the level brought up to the high mark. The difference between the two marks is about 0·5 litre. *Never overfill.*

If the unit is checked when cold, the level must not exceed a point 9·5 mm under the high mark. The need for frequent topping up indicates leakages which must be rectified immediately.

Adjustments
Periodic adjustments are not required under normal operating conditions.

Cable control
(a) Check the correct location of the cable stop at the carburettor end.
(b) Connect a tachometer to the engine and a pressure gauge to the transmission (special service tools).

(c) Select D and increase the engine speed from 500 rev/min to 1000 rev/min when the pressure should increase by between 97 kN/m² and 138 kN/m². The pressure rise is brought into the correct range by the use of the cable adjuster, increasing the pressure rise by increasing the length of the outer cable and reducing the pressure rise by reducing the length of the outer cable.

NOTE. The cable must not be oiled as it is impregnated by a molybdenum disulphide lubricant.

Faults which may result from the effective length of the outer cable being too short are (1) noise on take-up when D or R are selected and (2) difficult kick-down between top and second gear at high speeds. If the effective length of the outer cable is too long, then late and jerking lower speed up-shifts may occur. The down-shift from top to second gear at 40 km/h may also occur before the pedal detent touches the floor.

Rod control

This is linkage from the selector lever and it must never be allowed to override the cam detent, i.e. a distinct click must be felt in each selected position.

(a) Disconnect the linkage from the transmission lever.

(b) Set the lever in the central position of the five possible.

(c) Adjust the linkage to enable it to be connected without strain.

(d) Check for the correct operation of the linkage in all the selector positions. Lock the adjuster nut.

Accelerator detent

Check that the carburettor throttle valve is seven-eighths open when the pedal detent touches the floor.

Starter motor control (inhibitor) switch

The switch must only operate when P or N is selected.

The wiring to the switch may be checked by connecting together the leads to terminals 1 and 2, and the leads to 3 and 4. If the wiring is satisfactory the starting control and the reversing light will operate in all of the selector positions.

The switch may be adjusted by screwing it into and out of its boss on the unit housing, the leads being disconnected.

(a) Apply the hand brake and select D or L.

(b) Connect a small lamp and battery across terminals 1 and 2, and another lamp and battery across terminals 3 and 4.

(c) Screw the switch inward until contacts 3 and 4 break. Mark the switch position on the boss.

(d) Screw the switch farther inward until the contacts 1 and 2 make. Mark the switch position.

(e) Unscrew the switch until it is midway between the two marked positions. Tighten the locknut. Reconnect the leads.

(f) Check that the starter control operate only in P or N, and that the reverse lamp only lights when R is selected. If the operation is now incorrect the switch must be replaced.

Band adjustment

Rear band. The adjusting screw is external and is located in the right-hand wall of the housing. Slacken the locknut and tighten the adjusting screw to a torque loading of 14 Nm. Slacken the screw back by one turn and tighten the locknut.

Front band. The adjusting screw and locknut are internal and the sump of the unit must be removed. Cleanliness is essential. Slacken the lock-nut and move the servo lever outward. Place the special setting block (6·35 mm) between the screw and the servo piston pin, and tighten the adjusting screw to a torque loading of 1·13 Nm. Tighten the locknut. Remove the setting block and re-assemble the sump. Top up with the correct oil. Note that all work on these units should be carried out only with the aid of the special tools and instruments specified by the vehicle manufacturer.

NOTE. The same care in cleanliness, careful working, and careful handling that is accepted in operations with C.I. injection equipment must also be taken in all work carried out on automatic transmissions.

7

The Final Drive

The differential lock

The main feature of the conventional differential gear system is that it divides the available torque equally between the two half-shafts – although they may rotate at different speeds. Unfortunately this action depends upon the half-shafts having the same resistance to rotation, so when one road wheel slips upon a loose surface, i.e. offers no resistance to rotation, all of the available torque is transmitted to this slipping wheel. The rotation of the other wheel then ceases and the vehicle cannot move until the slipping wheel can be made to grip. Vehicles which have to be operated over loose surfaces must therefore have some means of putting the differential gearing out of action when wheel slip occurs, i.e. have some means of locking the differential gearing.

A simple differential lock consists of a dog clutch which can be moved to lock one half-shaft to either the crown wheel or the differential gear casing. This has the effect of locking the sun wheel of one half-shaft to the differential case – so locking the differential gearing and making the two half-shafts act as a solid shaft. The lock is engaged when one road wheel slips and the drive is maintained through the other road wheel. This mechanism is rather crude and has to be operated by the driver. It can only be engaged and released when the vehicle is stationary.

The limited-slip differential (Figure 7.1)

These units are very similar to the conventional differential but include devices which automatically lock the differential gearing when slip occurs at either road wheel. The normal action of the differential gearing still occurs during cornering, i.e. the outer wheel rotates faster than the inner wheel but wheel spin is reduced. Limited-slip, or non-slip, differential units are now used in many cars and commercial vehicles in addition to special-purpose military and civil-engineering vehicles.

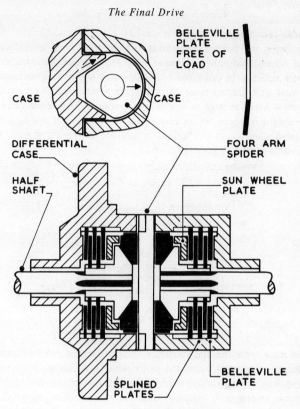

Fig. 7.1   Limited-slip differential

Several different types of limited-slip differential are in service but a feature common to them all is that a friction clutch is arranged between each sun wheel and the differential casing. The clutches are automatically engaged, i.e. the sun wheel locked to the casing, by (a) coil or Belleville springs, (b) the spider moving in a vee-shaped slot instead of being held in a close-fitting bore, or (c) the natural separating forces acting on the sun wheels. The engagement of either clutch locks its sun wheel to the differential casing and results in the maintenance of traction over poor ground, e.g. ice, snow, sand, gravel.

Double-reduction final drive (Figure 7.2)

The larger and heavier commercial vehicles must have large-diameter road wheels, and must operate at lower road speeds than smaller and lighter vehicles. In order to obtain the much higher torques required, the rear axle gearing must effect a much greater reduction in speed, the ratio being as high as 9:1 in some vehicles. This speed reduction and torque increase cannot reasonably be obtained by one step down in speed when a crown wheel and pinion are employed, so some form of double-reduction gearing is used.

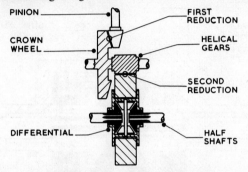

Fig. 7.2   Double-reduction final drive

In most types the first reduction of speed and increase in torque is obtained via a crown wheel and pinion which also changes the direction of the drive through ninety degrees. The second step down of speed and increase in torque is obtained either by the use of a pair of double helical gears, or by the use of a single epicyclic gear train. In each of these types the gearing is arranged at or near the centre of the rear axle.

An alternative type of double-reduction final drive has the first reduction provided via a crown wheel and pinion at or near the centre of the axle. The second reduction is provided by gearing arranged at the ends of the axle, the outer end of each half-shaft carrying a spur gear which drives an internally toothed ring gear attached to the hub of the wheel.

Two-speed final drive (Figure 7.3)

A low-ratio (high gear – less speed reduction) final drive will allow a good road speed under normal conditions, but will result in inadequate torque being available for hill climbing and carrying very heavy loads. A high-ratio (low gear – big speed reduction) final drive will provide adequate torque for very heavy loads and hill climbing, but only low road speeds will be possible.

Where vehicles may be operating with varying loads throughout the day, or delivering a heavy load and returning empty, it is more economical to be able to select the best final-drive gear ratio for the conditions applying to each journey. This can be done by the use of a two-speed axle which, in effect, doubles the number of available gearbox ratios.

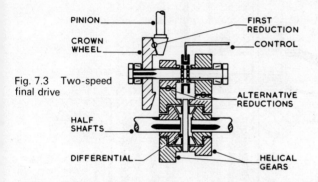

Fig. 7.3 Two-speed final drive

PINION

CROWN WHEEL

FIRST REDUCTION

CONTROL

ALTERNATIVE REDUCTIONS

HALF SHAFTS

DIFFERENTIAL

HELICAL GEARS

The first speed reduction and torque increase is effected by the use of a crown wheel and pinion. The second reduction is effected by the use of the two pairs of double helical gears. In the type shown the smaller gears run free on their shaft, and are locked to it by a central dog clutch when selected. There is no clutch neutral position and the helical gears are engaged with each other at all times. The differential gearing is arranged between the larger gears and supports the inner ends of the half-shafts. Taper roller bearings (opposed thrusts) are used throughout, and the ratios are about 6:1 or 8:1.

The vehicle is started from rest with the high ratio (low gear) selected. When top gear is reached in the gearbox, and if road conditions permit, the low ratio (high gear) of the final drive is engaged by declutching and moving the axle clutch manually, electrically, or by air pressure.

In an alternative arrangement the crown wheel drives the annulus of an epicyclic reduction gear train, the planets of which rotate the differential casing and spider via their shafts. High gear (low ratio) is obtained by locking the sun wheel of the epicyclic train to its annulus –

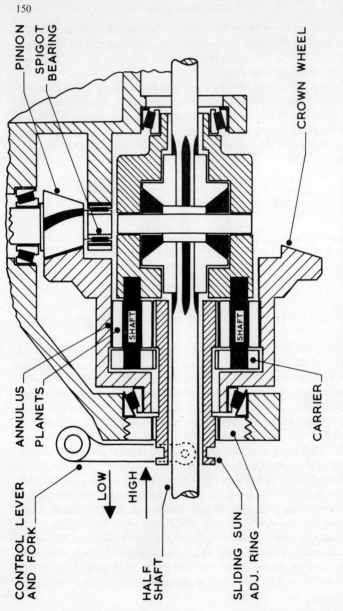

PINION

SPIGOT
BEARING

CROWN WHEEL

CONTROL LEVER
AND FORK

ANNULUS

PLANETS

LOW

HIGH

HALF
SHAFT

SLIDING SUN

ADJ. RING

SHAFT

SHAFT

CARRIER

Fig. 7.4 Two-speed final drive — alternative arrangement

thus locking up the train and rotating the differential case and spider at the same speed as the crown wheel. Low gear (high ratio) is obtained by locking the sun to a non-rotating housing, the planets being forced to rotate about the sun and rotate the differential case and spider at a speed less than that of the crown wheel.

Worm final drive (Figure 7.5)
In these types of final drive the reduction of speed and the corresponding increase in torque, and the necessary change of torque direction, are obtained by the use of a worm and wheel. The wheel is made of bronze and the worm of hardened alloy steel. The worm may not be parallel but hour-glass-shaped; this shape results in a larger area of tooth contact and lower end thrust forces. The worm and the wheel are supported and located by opposed-thrust, taper-roller, bearings – an extra bearing being fitted to control the end thrust. This will be at the end of the worm opposite from the driving flange in the single-drive axle and at the end nearest the driving flange in the double-drive type of axle. The worm may be arranged above or below the wheel to make possible either a greater ground clearance or a lower platform height, i.e. the worm may be overslung or underslung.

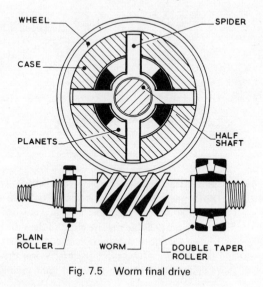

Fig. 7.5   Worm final drive

Worm final drives are very quiet in operation and are more efficient than most crown-wheel types, their power loss being about 2% as against the 4% to 5% of the crown-wheel type. Worm drives also have a much longer service life and require less adjustment. They are, however, very much more expensive to manufacture. Great care must be taken in their initial assembly and only the correct lubricant must be used. This must be checked at weekly intervals and changed at the correct intervals. The axle casing incorporates a fairly large sump which may be finned to dissipate excess heat.

Multi-drive axles (Figure 7.6)

These are used to reduce the load imposed upon any one wheel or axle, i.e. to spread the load. The maximum weight to be carried by any one axle is limited by law – to both protect the road surfaces and reduce possible accidents. It is also limited by the load a tyre can withstand. Wider tyres and twin-wheel axles can withstand heavier loads but when their weight limits have to be exceeded twin axles must be employed.

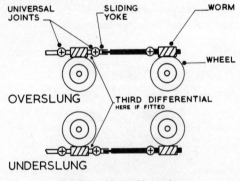

Fig. 7.6   Multi-drive axles

Most heavy commercial vehicles employ twin-wheel, twin-axle arrangements in which the rear end load is shared between the two axles. While it is possible for the rearmost axle to be a dead (non-driving) axle this reduces the possible tractive effort of the vehicle. Most twin-axle arrangements therefore incorporate two driving axles and these are usually of the worm-drive type, the first worm driving the second via a short shaft fitted with two universal joints and a sliding yoke. In some arrangements a differential unit is built into the output side of the first worm.

Split propeller shafts

In most cars, and particularly those in which the gearbox has an extended tailshaft, a single propeller shaft can be made sufficiently short and light in weight to provide a satisfactory service life. In the larger cars and commercial vehicles the use of one longer, and therefore heavier, shaft would result in excessive whip and vibration, and in excessive wear of universal and sliding joints. These difficulties are avoided in these longer vehicles by the use of two, and sometimes three, propeller shafts.

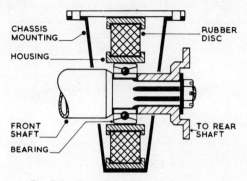

Fig. 7.7   Propeller shaft — centre bearing

The most common arrangement consists of a front and a rear shaft (see Fig. 7.7). The forward end of the front shaft carries a universal joint which is bolted to the output shaft of the gearbox. The rear end is supported by either a ball or a roller bearing which is itself supported in a rubber-mounted housing secured to the chassis. The bearing may need lubricating at intervals or be a sealed type.

The forward end of the rear shaft incorporates a universal joint and a sliding yoke which is bolted to the rear end of the front shaft. A universal joint at the rear end of the rear shaft is bolted to the pinion or the worm of the final drive unit.

Four-wheel drive (Figure 7.8)

Vehicles which are intended to operate over soft ground or loose surfaces, or across country, are so designed that all four wheels may be driven when required. In these vehicles a transfer gearbox is arranged centrally between the two axles. This gearbox is connected to the normal gearbox by a short shaft, and to the pinion of each axle by longer shafts – all three shafts having two universal joints and a sliding yoke each. Torque is normally transmitted from the gearbox to the rear axle only, via the transfer gearbox. When four-wheel drive is required and selected, the transfer gearbox transmits torque to the front shaft and axle as well as to the rear axle. This enables the vehicle to negotiate very bad ground in spite of wheel slip at one or more wheels.

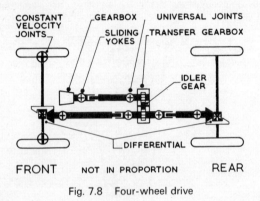

FRONT   NOT IN PROPORTION   REAR

Fig. 7.8   Four-wheel drive

Constant-velocity joints

The commonly used Hooke's type of universal joint has the serious disadvantage that it does not transmit torque at a constant velocity. If the driving shaft rotates at a constant speed, in one complete revolution the driven shaft has two periods in which it rotates at a speed higher than that of the driving shaft and two periods in which it rotates at a speed lower than the driving shaft – and the greater the angle between the two shafts the greater the variation in the velocities of the driven shaft.

This disadvantage may be overcome (as in the propeller shaft) by using two such joints, the speed increase of the one being neutralized by the speed reduction of the other – provided the yokes are correctly aligned with each other. Two universal joints of this type cannot be used, however, where the driven shaft has to operate at large or greatly varying angles from the driven shaft, and where space is limited, e.g. in driving/steering axles and in independent-suspension arrangements.

In these situations some form of constant-velocity joint is employed in which the centre part of the joint (in effect) automatically aligns itself on the plane bisecting the angle between the shafts. In order to make this automatic alignment possible, these joints have at least four effective parts instead of three, i.e. two yokes or their equivalent, and at least two centre parts. Examples of such joints are the Bendix Tracta and Weiss joints, and the Rzeppa joint.

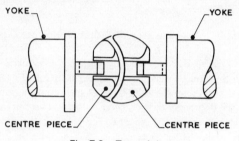

Fig. 7.9   Tracta joint

The Tracta joint (Fig. 7.9) has two centre pieces which join to form a sphere. Each piece is so shaped and slotted that it can move on the other, and the flat yokes are fitted into additional slots in their outer faces. The yokes and centre pieces realign themselves continuously as the joint rotates and so keep the velocity of the driven shaft constant.

In the Weiss joints, each yoke has two or three curved arms, semi-circular grooves being machined in the sides of each arm. The arms of the two yokes intersect and steel balls, fitting in the grooves, transmit the drive from one yoke to the other. The grooves are so shaped that as the joint rotates the balls automatically move to maintain their position in the plane of the angle bisecting the angle between the two shafts – this being the essential requirement for obtaining constant velocity at the driven shaft.

The Rzeppa joint (Fig. 7.10) has cup-shaped and ball-shaped members instead of yokes. The cup has semicircular grooves in its inner surface, and the ball matching grooves in its outer face. A steel ball is fitted into each groove and all the balls are located by a cage. As the joint rotates, and the angle between the shafts alters, the changes

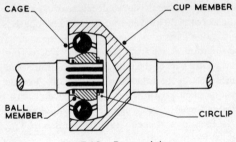

Fig. 7.10   Rzeppa joint

are followed by the cage to keep the balls in the plane of the bisecting angle.

Another type of constant-velocity joint is the Hooke's joint (Fig. 7.11) in which a four-legged cross or spider is mounted in split rubber bushes. The bushes are enclosed by steel shells and the rubber is pre-loaded by the tightening of shouldered U bolts. These fit into grooves in the shells and secure the spider to the yokes. The flexibility of the rubber allows the spider to centralize itself as the joint rotates – so maintaining constant velocity. It also reduces the transmission of shock loads and vibration. This type of joint permits large angular variations between the two shafts, has a long service life, and requires no regular attention.

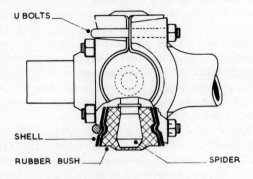

Fig. 7.11   Hooke's rubber joint

8 The Chassis and Suspension

The frame or chassis provides a mounting for the major working assemblies, and maintains them in their correct positions relative to each other, i.e. resists the forces acting upon them.

The chassis may be considered as a beam supported at two points, the various loads to which it is subjected acting at points along its length. Under these conditions the upper part of the beam is subjected to compressive stress and the lower part to tensile stress. Both forms of stress progressively reduce towards the centre of the beam where a line of zero or neutral stress will exist.

The strength of the beam must *never* be reduced by the ignorant or careless siting of drilled holes. When holes have to be drilled through the beam during repair or other work they *must* be located only in either the neutral or the compressive stress areas. A hole drilled in the tensile stress area will weaken the beam – the edges of the hole pulling away from the rivet or bolt, and cracking or splitting resulting.

Separate chassis–body types

In these the chassis also provides a mounting for the body. The body adds weight, but very little strength, to the assembly and the chassis must be made as rigid as possible to resist flexing and distortion due to uneven road surfaces. The usual construction consists of two long side frames with shorter cross-members. In the early forms of this construction these frame members were similar to those used for commercial vehicles, i.e. very heavy steel pressings but the later forms had box or channel section members which were just as strong but much lighter in weight. The side frames were much deeper in section between the wheels to provide extra strength against bending loads, and were swept up at front and rear to permit the movement of the axles. In plan they are closer at the forward end to permit the use of a larger steering lock and therefore a smaller turning circle. The cross-members were of box, channel, or tubular section and were bolted, riveted, or welded to the side frames. Additional cross bracing was provided to resist the effect of engine torque reaction.

When Independent Front Suspension (IFS) is used with this type of chassis the forward upsweep is reduced. This is because space is not required to allow for the front axle movement. The engine is then arranged lower in the chassis – so bringing the centre of gravity of the vehicle nearer to the ground and improving the road-holding qualities of the vehicle. The forward end of this type of chassis must be very heavily reinforced to enable the side frames to resist the torsional forces of the suspension arms.

Combined chassis-floor

The earlier types of separate chassis had a floor of plywood panels. These added weight but not strength – and rotted – and the later (pressed sheet steel) types had a floor of fluted, light-gauge, mild steel sheet. This was welded to the side and cross members, the combination of fluting and welding resulting in a light but rigid chassis suitable for both cars and light commercial vehicles. In all of these separate chassis types the body was bolted to the chassis, and insulated from it by felt or rubber strips to reduce vibration and noise.

Integral construction

This is the modern form of construction for light commercial vehicles and all but the heaviest cars. It is light in weight, and economical when produced in very large numbers. In this construction a very large number of light-gauge, mild steel, pressings are correctly aligned and welded together to form a one-piece unit of chassis, floor, and body. The loads are spread over the whole assembly so that it is very strong although very light in weight. See Plates 1 and 2, page 167.

Damaged sections may be removed by drilling through the spot welds, and new sections fitted with the aid of alignment jigs and spot or gas welding techniques. Sub-frames are often used for units such as the engine and suspension arrangements. These are usually attached to the main assembly by rubber mountings to prevent or reduce the transmission of their operating noise to the body shell.

This form of construction, due to the light gauge of mild steel sheet used, is very susceptible to damage by corrosion. Water drain holes in enclosed sections must be cleared periodically, and it is advisable to paint, or use chemical methods to protect, the interior surfaces of these sections. Regular washing of the undersides of the vehicle during the winter, and undersealing, are also helpful in obtaining a longer lasting body shell and frames.

COMMERCIAL-VEHICLE CHASSIS

Goods vehicles are designed to carry heavy loads but they must conform to the legal limits of width and axle loading. They must also be within acceptable limits of cost in terms of tons carried per mile. The chassis has to be much more rigid than is required for lighter vehicles and the side frames are forgings of much heavier gauge steel plate. They are deeper in section, and more and deeper section cross-members are essential although cross bracing is seldom used. The cross-members are hot riveted to the side frames and wide gusset plates are added to make the assembly more rigid.

Where twin wheel axles are used to make possible the carrying of heavier loads the width of the chassis must be reduced (width limitation of the vehicle). The necessary rigidity can then only be obtained by making the chassis stronger and heavier than where single wheels are employed.

Damaged side frames must be removed for straightening, and if bending through less than 10° is involved it should be done cold. Hot straightening should be carried out at between 750 °C and 850 °C. The necessary maximum tightness of joints can only be obtained by hot riveting during rebuilding. Emergency repairs only may be carried out by reaming the distorted rivet hole to the next oversize and fitting high tensile steel bolts, and lock washers or plates.

Where the axles are attached to a single chassis the chassis is classed as a rigid type. Articulated types are those which consist of a tractor and trailer unit which are designed to operate together, the forward end of the trailer being supported and drawn along by the tractor.

Rigid types (Figure 8.1)
These include four, six, and eight-wheeled types, the driving wheels being single or twin types. Six-wheeled vehicles usually have two steering road wheels and either two driving axles or one driving axle

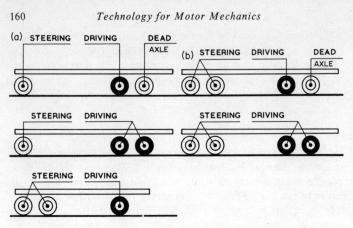

Fig. 8.1 Rigid types. Six-wheelers (*left*) and eight-wheelers

and one dead axle. Eight wheelers have four steering road wheels and either two driving axles or one driving axle and one dead axle.

These vehicles use the load to increase the adhesion between the road and the tyres of their driving wheels. The extra length of the six and eight wheelers makes them difficult to manœuvre in small areas as they have a large turning circle.

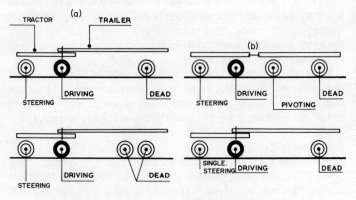

Fig. 8.2 Articulated types: three wheeled tractor

Articulated types (Figure 8.2)

Advantages over rigid types

(1) Greater manœuvrability due to the articulation and the small turning circle of the tractor unit.
(2) Greater work output – the detaching of the trailer for loading and unloading leaving the tractor free to do other work.

Disadvantages

(1) Less adhesion between the road and the driving wheels – the greater part of the load being carried by the dead axles of the trailer.
(2) More care needed by the driver – due to the limited arc of movement of the coupling mechanism and the possibility of the trailer over-running the tractor (jack-knifing).
(3) Unsuitable for use over very uneven ground, and particularly across side slopes.

The tractor unit may have one or two driving axles, the trailers having one or two dead axles. Trailers used with rigid types of chassis are usually two axle types, the forward axle swivelling for steering purposes.

SUSPENSION ARRANGEMENTS

Springs

The tyres reduce the shock transmitted by road irregularities to the wheels, and the springs are arranged between the wheels and the body to reduce the shock transmitted from the wheels to the body. Springs may be of steel, rubber, or air, steel springs being the most common. These may be leaf, coil, or torsion bar types and are made from a strong and fatigue resistance silicon–manganese steel.

Although the larger commercial vehicles still have leaf springs for both front and rear suspension most modern cars and light commercial vehicles have leaf springs in the rear suspension only.

The 'rate' of a leaf spring or its stiffness (force required to deflect it by 25·4 mm) is determined by its length, width, thickness, and number of leaves. The shorter the spring, and the wider, thicker, and more numerous its leaves the greater its rate – and the harder the ride. Low rate springs provide a softer ride but the wheel takes longer to return to the road after being deflected. In a normal spring (where the leaves all have the same camber) the rate is constant. A spring in which the lower leaves have the camber reversed has a variable rate, stiffening as the deflection brings the lower leaves into action.

Leaf springs have a natural damping (energy absorbing) action due to friction between the leaves but as this varies and results in wear the friction is reduced by the use of interleaving of soft materials. These may be brass, zinc, or rubber strips or nylon or rubber buttons fitted at the leaf ends. Hydraulic dampers are used which can be relied upon to provide constant and accurate damping.

Coil and torsion bar springs have no natural damping, and their rate depends upon their length and diameter – increasing the length or reducing the diameter reducing the rate.

Rubber springs utilize rubber arranged in compression or shear and they may be used as either main or auxiliary springs. They have the advantages of increasing their rate as the deflection is increased, and of releasing less energy than they receive.

Air springs consist of a volume of air enclosed in either a steel cylinder or a bellows of heavy duty rubber. Air is supplied to or exhausted from the bellow through the action of a control valve operated by the movement of the chassis relative to the axles. Air springs thus make possible the maintaining of a constant platform height in spite of varying loads, and they have a variable rate – heavier loads increasing the rate.

FRONT SUSPENSIONS

The design of the chassis, the suspension, and the steering must be coordinated as the features of one affects the features of the other two. The brake system must also be considered.

Cars, and many of the lighter commercial vehicles, are now fitted with some form of Independent Front Suspension (IFS). See Plate 3. These have the following advantages over the earlier beam axle and leaf spring arrangements:

(1) Much less unsprung weight.
(2) The steering is not affected by the gyroscopic effect of a deflected wheel being transmitted to the other wheel.
(3) Better steering stability due to the wider spacing of the springs.
(4) Better road holding as the centre of gravity is lower – due to the engine being arranged nearer to the ground.
(5) More space in the body due to the engine being lower and possibly farther forward.

(6) More comfortable ride due to the use of lower rate springs.

Where a beam axle and parallel leaf spring arrangement is used the springs are subjected to the following forces:

(a) Suspension loads due to vehicle weight.

(b) Driving and braking thrusts due respectively to the forward movement of the chassis, and its retardation when braking.

(c) Braking torque reaction – the spring distorting but preventing the rotating of the backplate and axle.

(d) Twisting due to the deflection of one wheel only.

When the springs are strong enough to resist all these forces they are too stiff and heavy to provide a comfortable ride and good road holding. IFS designs must provide for the control or limitation of these same forces, and their action must not interfere with the steering geometry or the operation of the braking system.

Independent front suspension

Parallel link (coil spring)
This is a commonly used design in which a large helical steel spring is arranged between two suspension arms (see Fig. 8.3). The arms are wishbone shaped, the lower end of the spring locating in a plate fitted to the lower arm. The upper end of the spring is located in an inverted

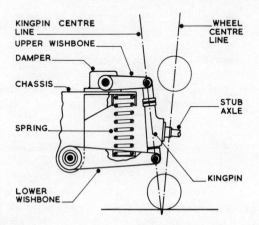

Fig. 8.3   Coil-spring type

cup forming part of the chassis frame. The lower arm is secured to the chassis by either screwed bushes or rubber bushes. The upper arm may be secured in the same manner or it may be splined to the spindle of the damper unit bolted to the chassis. As an alternative a tubular type of damper may be fitted inside the spring and secured to the lower arm and the cup. The stub axle and kingpin assembly are secured to the outer ends of the arms by ball joints or trunnions.

Where the arms or links are of equal length the deflection of the wheel alters the steering track and causes excessive tyre wear. In most arrangements of this type the upper arm is shorter than the lower and this results in the track remaining almost constant – but the camber angle is altered. The castor angle is obtained by arranging the upper arm slightly to the rear of the lower arm.

Braking torque is resisted by the wide spacing of the inner ends of the lower arm, and the axis of these ends is at an angle to the axis of the vehicle. This permits the lower mounting of the engine to improve road holding, and the use of longer arms.

Parallel link (torsion bar)

The kingpin and the arm arrangement is very similar to that used with a coil spring, the spring being replaced by a longitudinally arranged torsion bar (see Fig. 8.4). This may be a solid or a laminated type, one

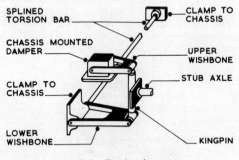

Fig. 8.4   Torsion-bar type

end of which is secured to the chassis in a splined clamp plate while the other end is splined into the inner end of the lower wishbone arm. The number of splines at each end of the bar are different so a vernier effect is obtained which makes possible the re-adjustment of the chassis height. This may become necessary if the torsion bar should take up a permanent twist due to an overload (suspension settle).

An alternative arrangement consists of two I section arms and a radius rod. The rod is fitted between the outer end of the lower arm and the chassis at a point behind the arm mounting. The rod is used to resist the braking torque and the thrust forces. A longitudinal torsion bar may be connected to the lower arm, or a coil spring arranged above the upper arm. In some variations a rubber spring with a short link arm is arranged above the upper arm.

Telescopic (Macpherson strut) type
In this arrangement (Fig. 8.5) the stub axle is integral with the lower part of a telescopic tube which incorporates a tubular hydraulic damper.

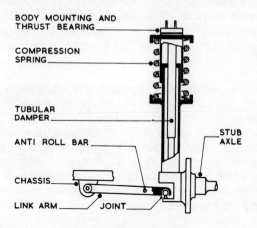

Fig. 8.5   Telescopic type

The lower part is attached to the outer end of a link arm by a ball joint, the inner end of the arm being secured to the chassis. The upper end of the tube is secured to the body via a thrust bearing which prevents the longitudinal movement of the upper end but allows the complete tube to swivel. A coil spring is fitted between the upper and lower parts of the tube. The caster, camber, and kingpin inclination angles cannot be adjusted in service and the link arm controls the track.

Swing arm type

In one design (Fig. 8.6) two short torsion bars are arranged one above the other and across the chassis. The inner end of each bar is splined into a mounting secured to the chassis while a trailing arm is splined

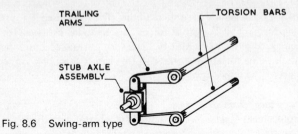

Fig. 8.6   Swing-arm type

to the outer end of each bar. The kingpin and stub axle assembly is carried between the ends of the trailing arms. In other designs the arms may lead instead of trail, and the torsion bars may be replaced by rubber springs. Hydraulic dampers are connected to the upper arms.

Anti-roll bars

These transversely arranged, 'U' shaped, steel bars are secured to the lower arms of the front suspension units at each side of the vehicle. They may sometimes also be fitted between the arms of piston type hydraulic dampers at the rear of the vehicle. They improve the handling of the vehicle by acting as torsion bars, increasing the roll frequency by stiffening the suspension as roll occurs. Pitching is another fault which adversely affects the handling of the vehicle. Pitch is minimized by the design of the suspension and dampers such that the bounce frequency at the front end is lower than that of the rear end.

REAR SUSPENSION

The most commonly used rear suspension is the leaf spring arrangement – in which the forward end of the spring at each side of the vehicle is secured directly to the chassis while the rear ends are secured by swing shackles. The axle may be arranged over or under the springs, and may be insulated from them by rubber pads.

The forces acting on the springs, due to the action of the driving axle, are:

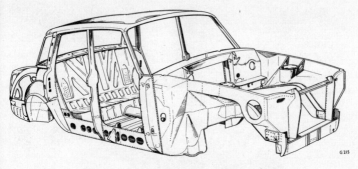

Plate 1   Body construction – Rolls Royce

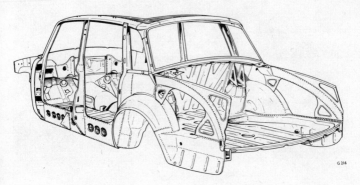

Plate 2   Body construction – Rolls Royce

Plate 3   Front suspension and sub-frame – Rolls Royce

Plate 4   Rear suspension and sub-frame – Rolls Royce

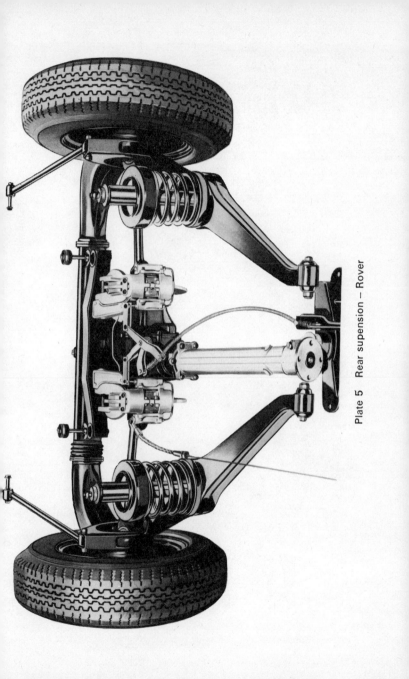

Plate 5   Rear supension – Rover

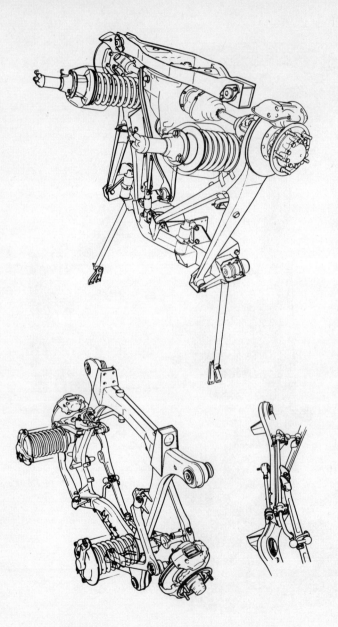

Plate 6   Suspensions and sub-frames — Rolls Royce

(a) Bending loads due to the weight and load of the vehicle.

(b) Torsion or twisting – when one wheel only is deflected.

(c) The driving and braking thrusts – transferring the axle motion to the chassis.

(d) The driving and braking torque reaction forces – resisting the rotation of the axle case.

These forces act at all driving axles and must be limited whatever the design of the rear suspension.

Independent rear suspension

Although most of the advantages of springing the front wheels independently also apply to the rear wheels the major advantage of IRS lies in the very large reduction of unsprung weight which can be obtained – particularly where both the brakes and the final drive are secured to the chassis or sub-frame. See Plates 4, 5 and 6.

Transverse spring (Figure 8.7)

In one arrangement the spring is mounted above the final drive, both being attached to the chassis. The upper ends of the wheel bearing supports are attached to the ends of the spring, and the lower ends to tubular dampers. These are inclined and their upper ends are secured in rigid arms which form part of the sub-frame. The half-shafts are driven via universal joints at the differential end.

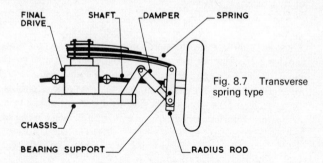

Fig. 8.7 Transverse spring type

Swing arm

In these arrangements the wheel bearing assembly is mounted in the rear end of an arm which swings from a bearing on the sub or main frame. The final drive is secured to the sub-frame. The half-shafts may have two universal joints or one constant-velocity joint. The movement of the swing arms may be controlled by torsion bars, coil springs, rubber springs, or a transverse leaf spring. Radius rods may be fitted between the sub-frame and the swing arms, and tubular dampers between the arms and the main frame or chassis.

Swinging half-axle (Figure 8.8)

The road wheels and rear axle tubes are pivoted at the final drive which is secured to the chassis. Coil springs are fitted between the chassis and the outer ends of the axle tubes, together with inclined tubular

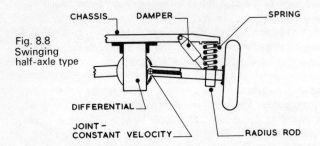

Fig. 8.8
Swinging
half-axle type

dampers. The axle ends are located by radius rods, and the half-shafts are driven via constant-velocity joints arranged at the centre of swing of each axle.

Parallel link

These are similar to the torsion bar type of IFS, the hub bearing unit replacing the kingpin assembly. The half-shafts have two universal joints of the wide angle type. Due to the length of arm required this arrangement is usually limited to the backbone type of chassis.

NOTE. These independent suspension arrangements can all be modified to operate with air springs, the metal springs being replaced by air bellows or cylinders.

Hydrolastic suspension (Figure 8.9)

In these systems rubber springs at each wheel are actuated by hydraulic pressure, the front and rear units at each side being connected by a pipe. When one wheel is deflected its movement forces a tapered piston to move upward and increase the pressure on the fluid – so bringing a

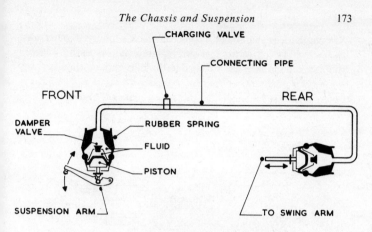

Fig. 8.9   Hydrolastic suspension

conical rubber spring into action. At the same time the fluid is directed into the mating spring which is forced down. This action eliminates the pitching of the vehicle, and its roll resistance is increased by the increase in fluid pressure in both springs. As the fluid absorbs shock loads external dampers are not required.

Commercial-vehicle rear suspension

Single axle
These are similar in arrangement but stronger in construction than those used for cars.

Double axle
These are designed as a combined unit and are known as bogies. The main points of the design are that the loads carried by the axles remain approximately the same under all operating conditions, and that the axles be kept as close to each other as possible. This is to reduce the tendency to skidding which results from the wheels being unable to align themselves at right angles to their radius of turn.

In the balance beam arrangement the springs are arranged on each side of the beam, the deflection of one axle forcing the other down to maintain the sharing of the load. As the beam must be kept short to avoid skidding this arrangement is suitable only for vehicles operating over good surfaces.

In another design of bogie a trunnion block is mounted at the side of the chassis. Two inverted leaf springs are clamped to the swivelling trunnion and the axles are attached to the ends of the springs.

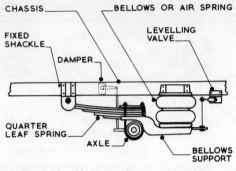

Fig. 8.10   Air suspension – arrangement

Air suspension (Figures 8.10 and 8.11)

Air suspension systems are used by a number of passenger-carrying vehicles, and by some special service vehicles, and trailers. In one arrangement a quarter-elliptical leaf spring is shackled to the chassis at its forward end. The rear end is secured to the axle, together with a support for the underside of a two-lobe bellows type of air spring. The

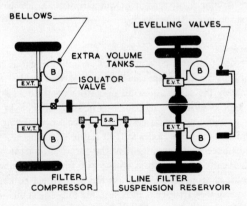

Fig. 8.11   Air suspension – system

upper end of the spring is located by a bracket secured to the chassis. Piston or lever type dampers are fitted between the axle and the chassis, and the movement of the bellows support operates an air-levelling valve. Extra volume tanks are fitted near the bellows and are connected to the bellows by pipes. An engine-driven air compressor supplies air to a suspension reservoir. Where two bellows on opposite sides of the vehicle are controlled by one levelling valve an isolator valve is fitted which controls cross flow to maintain the roll resistance. In this arrangement the sideways movement of the axle is prevented by the use of a Panhard rod fitted between the end of the axle and the chassis at the opposite side.

In another arrangement a semi-elliptical leaf spring of light construction is used to locate the axle and limit torque reaction. The spring takes some of the unladen weight but the full load is taken by two air springs. These are arranged on each side of the axle and under the springs, being supported by their own carrier clamped to the axle.

Rubber suspension
One of the best-known systems is that of the toggle-link suspension (Fig. 8.12) which is used for many bus axles. In the simplest terms two

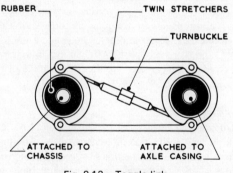

RUBBER — TWIN STRETCHERS

TURNBUCKLE

ATTACHED TO CHASSIS

ATTACHED TO AXLE CASING

Fig. 8.12   Toggle link

bonded rubber bushes are arranged at each side of the axle and their steel outer cases are connected by top and bottom stretchers. The hubs of the bushes nearest the axle are secured to it, the hubs of the other bushes being secured to the chassis. The links are so arranged that the bushes are concentric under normal load, being distorted as the load is increased. The four links form the complete suspension (Fig. 8.13) and control the forces acting upon the axle. The bushes and links are splayed to widen the base of the system, so increasing the roll resistance.

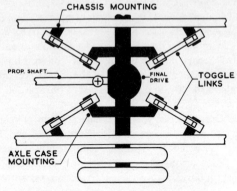

Fig. 8.13   Toggle-link arrangement

Dampers

Good road holding, safety, and comfort depend upon the correct selection, installation, and maintenance of the dampers. These are all hydraulic types and operate by converting the energy given to the spring into heat. The heat results from forcing oil to pass through restriction valves from one chamber to another. The temperature of the oil may reach 140 °C and there may be 12,500 fluid oscillations per kilometre. The main types of damper used are the piston and lever type, and the tubular type.

Piston and lever type

The construction and valve detail are illustrated in Figs. 8.14 and 8.15. Note that the valves are not interchangeable – loadings may vary between front and rear and sometimes between each side of the vehicle.

When the wheel is deflected the oil pressure built up forces the compression valve from its seat and forces the oil to pass into the second cylinder. Although the rebound valve is moved bodily it does not operate. When the spring rebounds the oil pressure forces the rebound valve to move down the rod and away from its seat, the oil passing back into the first cylinder. Slight wheel deflections do not open the valves but the oil passes from one cylinder to the other via a small

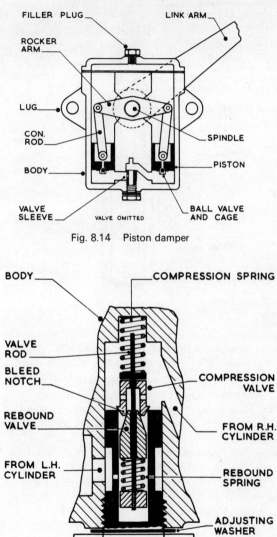

Fig. 8.14 Piston damper

Fig. 8.15 Valve detail

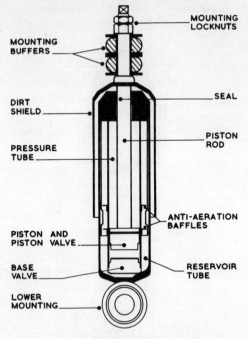

Fig. 8.16   Tubular damper

notch cut in the face of the compression valve. This notch also reduces the possible build up of excessive pressures. As each piston rises its ball valve is opened to permit the escape of any air trapped below it and the complete filling of the cylinder by oil, i.e. automatic recuperation occurs.

Some valve systems have automatic compensation for the temperature changes which affect oil viscosity. Others have adjustable settings.

Tubular type (Figure 8.16)

These are used where spring deflections are relatively large. When inclined they can provide some degree of roll resistance, and they are often incorporated inside IFS arrangements.

The tubular damper consists of a central pressure tube surrounded by a reservoir tube. A base valve is fitted in this tube to control the movement of fluid between the two tubes. As the unit is subjected to violent movement the reservoir tube has some device to prevent fluid frothing. This would render the unit inoperative as air can be compressed. The pressure and reservoir tubes are filled with fluid and are sealed to form one unit. Rubber bushed mounting eyes or stems are integral. The pressure tube encloses a sliding piston and valve assembly carried at the lower end of a piston rod, the upper end carrying the mounting. The piston rod is protected by a dirt shield welded to the rod.

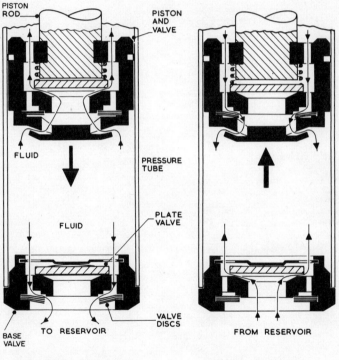

PISTON ROD

PISTON AND VALVE

FLUID

PRESSURE TUBE

FLUID

PLATE VALVE

TO RESERVOIR

VALVE DISCS

BASE VALVE

FROM RESERVOIR

Fig. 8.17   Compression   Fig. 8.18   Extension

Figs. 8.17 and 8.18 show the action of the valves and the flow of fluid as the damper is compressed and extended as the result of rapid spring movements. If the compression is slow the fluid passes through bleed notches in the base valve discs into the reservoir. Similarly if the extension is slow fluid passes through bleed notches in the piston valve discs from the space above the piston.

Service

The modern tendency is for dampers to be sealed – and replaced when no longer efficient. Mounting brackets and bushes must be checked at regular intervals. In most types adjustments are not possible but manufacturers will advise in cases of particular difficulty.

The shock-absorbing qualities of a tyre are derived from its deflection under load, the greater the deflection the more comfortable the ride. Modern low-pressure tyres have deflection rates designed to suit the vehicle, i.e. the higher the speed the less the deflection. Radial-ply tyres have a larger deflection than cross-ply tyres, and at speeds in excess of about 65 km/h provide a comfortable ride with an increased grip on the road. At lower speeds the stiffness of the bracing cords has a greater effect and the ride is less comfortable.

The rated load per wheel supported by a correctly inflated tyre varies from about 35 to 50 times the weight of the tyre – depending on the type of vehicle and the construction of the tyre.

About 95% of the power loss due to the tyres results from the production of heat. Prolonged high-speed running reduces the life of the tyres by reducing the strength and other mechanical properties of the materials used in their construction. Tyres with treads of synthetic rubber tend to run at higher temperatures but have the advantages of increased grip and greater wear resistance.

Slip angles (Figure 9.1)

When a wheel and tyre assembly is steered, i.e. moved away from the direction in which it is travelling, the angular difference between the aimed direction and the direction of motion is known as the slip or creep angle (slip does not actually occur). Under these circumstances the centre line of the tread is deflected as it contacts the ground and the reaction from the road generates a cornering force which acts behind the centre of the contact area of the tread. The size of this force per slip-angle degree is known as the cornering power, and cornering power depends largely upon the design of the tyre and its inflation pressure.

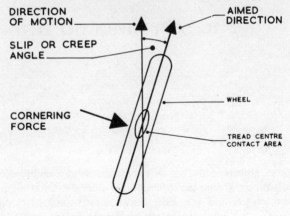

Fig. 9.1   Slip angle

Self-aligning torque (Figure 9.2)

As the cornering force acts behind the centre of tread contact area the tyre tries to align itself in the direction of motion, i.e. cornering force generates a self-aligning torque. This torque can be varied by altering the kingpin inclination angle.

When a driver turns his steering wheel he alters the slip angles of the front wheels and so varies the sizes of the cornering forces – larger slip angles increasing the cornering forces until a point is reached where the grip of the treads on the road surface is lost.

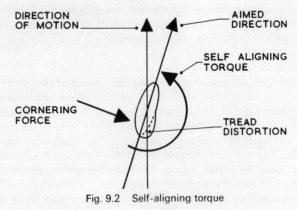

Fig. 9.2   Self-aligning torque

Tyre grip

The grip, or adhesion, of the tyres limits the cornering power of the vehicle, and is the governing factor in the efficiency of the brakes, and limits the rate of acceleration.

On dry, rough, road surfaces the coefficient of friction between a tyre and the road is between 0·8 and 0·9 – and there is no practical difference between the coefficients of a smooth and a new tyre.

On wet, rough, road surfaces the function of the tread pattern is to break up the surface of the water film so that dry rubber contacts dry road, the coefficient of friction being about 0·6 to 0·7 and reducing with smoother road surfaces. Where a depth of water of up to about 2 mm exists, the tread must squeeze the water towards the sides and rear of the contacting tread blocks before breaking the film to make dry contact. The efficiency with which the film is broken and the excess water is squeezed away is determined largely by the design of the tread pattern. The grip is largely determined by the type of rubber used for the tread. Note particularly that a smooth tyre has no grip on a wet surface because the water acts as a lubricant.

Strong and heavy tread patterns will normally provide an adequate grip in wet mud, slush, and fresh snow. Grip can only be obtained on ice when metal is used to penetrate the surface, e.g. when steel studs or wire claws are set into the tread, or chains are fitted over the tread – the tread pattern alone having no effect on the surface.

Oversteer and understeer (Figure 9.3)

The Ackerman or basic steering geometry is correct only at low speeds, and with solid or high-pressure tyres and stiff suspensions. In modern high-speed vehicles with low-pressure, high-deflection tyres and soft suspensions the centre of turn does *not lie on the axis of the rear axle produced*. Its location varies with the speed of the vehicle and the tightness of the turn but always lies on the line passing through the centre of gravity of the vehicle, and at some point closer to the vehicle than the basic centre of turn. As the rear wheels cannot align themselves at a right angle to their radius of turn they cannot rotate truly, and therefore the rear wheels also have slip angles and cornering power.

Where the slip angles of the front wheels are greater than those of the rear wheels, the vehicle turns at a radius larger than that intended, and the driver has to keep steering into the turn. This condition is known as understeer, and as it involves a more natural reaction from the

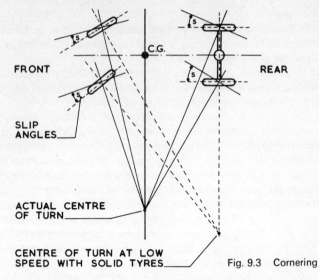

Fig. 9.3 Cornering

driver it is to be preferred rather than oversteer. Oversteer occurs when the slip angles of the front wheels are smaller than those of the rear wheels. The vehicle tightens into the turn and the driver has to keep straightening out as he negotiates a curve. Neutral steer occurs where the front and rear slip angles are the same.

The slip angles may be varied by design between the front and rear wheels, and between the wheels at each side front and rear. They may

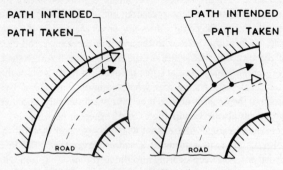

Fig. 9.4 Understeer (*left*) and oversteer

also alter due to the forces acting under different conditions. The front-to-rear slip-angle relationship may be altered by tyre pressures, types, and sizes. The driving and braking torques can alter the slip angles and cornering forces by distorting the tyres. Wheel camber, roll stiffness, and weight transfer on cornering can alter the side-to-side relationship of the slip angles. Understeer and oversteer can therefore alter in service if wear, neglect, or careless handling result in changes to one or more of the above features.

Twin steering axles (Figure 9.5)
Multi-axle arrangements are used to keep the weight carried by each axle and wheel within the legal limits. In some six-wheeled vehicles a twin-wheel rear axle is used with twin steering axles, a twin-wheel axle being unsuitable for steering purposes. In these arrangements the centre

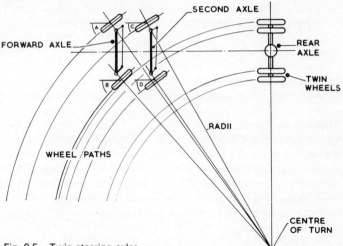

Fig. 9.5   Twin steering axles

of turn lies on a line midway between the rear axles, and the wheels of the foremost axle are swivelled through smaller angles than those of the second axle. This is made possible by the action of a double drop-arm system with an interconnecting drag link. The slip angles of the rear wheels are kept as small as possible to reduce the skid tendency by minimizing the distance between the rear axles (see rear axles).

POWER STEERING

With the increasing use of self-aligning torques, larger-deflection tyres, and heavier wheel loadings, power steering is rapidly becoming an essential feature of the steering systems of commercial vehicles and the heavier cars.

Advantages

(1) Reduction in the number of turns of the steering wheel from lock to lock, i.e. quicker steering, especially at high speeds.

(2) Reduction in the effort to be made by the driver, especially during low-speed manœuvring.

(3) Reduction of wheel wobble.

(4) Increased safety – an extreme road shock or a burst tyre cannot deflect the steering to a dangerous extent.

(5) More responsive and sensitive steering, together with an almost complete absence of steering-wheel shock and vibration.

Disadvantages

(1) Increased complication, weight, and cost.

(2) Increased maintenance.

(3) Additional power source required for pressurizing fluid or air.

System characteristics

Whatever power source or arrangement is employed, the power steering system must be capable of manual operation if power assistance should fail. Some free play will always be experienced and the manual effort required will be considerable. The system must also allow the driver to sense his steering – this result being obtained by making it necessary for him to apply a fairly large torque at the steering wheel before power assistance is provided.

Types

Two main types of system are in service, the integral and the link or jack types. Both may be powered by either fluid or air pressure, the units being similar but differing in arrangement on the vehicle.

Units

The following units are incorporated in a hydraulic system:

(1) A fluid reservoir.
(2) A belt-driven, rotor-type pump which can build up pressures of up to 6900 kN/m².
(3) An hydraulic accumulator or pressure reservoir.
(4) A power cylinder, or ram, with a double-acting piston.
(5) A control valve which is operated by the movement of either the steering wheel or the drop arm of the steering gearbox, and which is sensitive to the swivelling resistance of the road wheels.

The equivalent units are incorporated in the compressed-air systems, these often being employed where compressed air is already available for other systems.

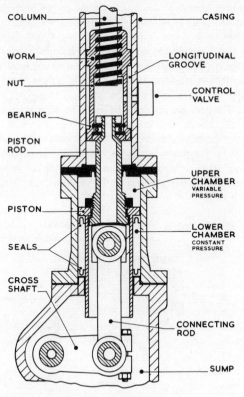

Fig. 9.6   Integral type

Integral system

In these systems the power cylinder and the control valve are built into, or alongside, the steering column and gearbox. The valves are usually operated by the movement of the steering wheel rather than the drop arm, and may be of the rotary type.

Construction (Figure 9.6)

In the Lockheed system for heavy vehicles the power cylinder and the control valve are built into the steering column and are arranged between the steering nut and the drop arm. The steering-wheel shaft has an integral worm which is engaged with a long bronze nut, the nut having a longitudinal groove in which is fitted one end of the bell crank lever of the control valve. The lower end of the nut carries a ball thrust bearing which supports and locates the upper end of a hollow piston rod in such a way that the nut can turn on the rod but longitudinal movement between them is prevented. The piston rod carries a double-faced piston which divides the cylinder into upper and lower pressure chambers.

The upper-face area of the piston is exactly twice that of the lower-face area. The pressure acting in the lower chamber is maintained constant at $6900 \, kN/m^2$ and the required degree of power assistance is obtained by the valve altering the pressure acting in the upper chamber (see Fig. 9.7). The pressure may be varied from atmospheric to up to $6900 \, kN/m^2$, the resulting differences between the *forces* acting on the piston causing it to move and assist the movement of the nut along the

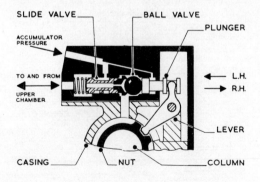

Fig. 9.7   Control valve

worm. The lower part of the piston is connected to the sector shaft and drop arm by twin connecting rods, and a sump is formed in the bottom of the column.

Operation

Minimum wheel-swivelling resistance. The frictional forces between the nut and the worm are minimal, and the nut is prevented from turning by the bell crank lever of the control valve. As the lever does not move the valve is inoperative, and the pressure of $3450 \, kN/m^2$ in the upper chamber produces a downward force on the piston which is exactly opposed by the upward force due to the constant pressure of $6900 \, kN/m^2$ in the lower chamber (remember area ratio). The piston therefore does not move and the nut is wound along the worm by manual effort alone.

Maximum wheel-swivelling resistance. The frictional forces between the nut and the worm are at the maximum, and the nut turns with the worm to the limit allowed by the valve lever. On a right-hand turn the lever movement allows the ball valve to move away from its seat on the slide valve, so allowing fluid to escape back to the sump from the upper chamber. The upward force on the piston, due to the constant pressure in the lower chamber, is no longer opposed and the piston is forced to move upward – so providing the maximum assistance to the upward movement of the nut on the worm, and to the swivelling of the wheels to the right. On a left-hand turn the lever movement forces the ball valve to move the slide valve. The bevel face of this valve is forced away from its seating and the full accumulator pressure of $6900 \, kN/m^2$ is allowed to act in the upper chamber. The maximum difference between the two forces causes the piston to move down and provide the maximum assistance to the downward movement of the nut, and to the swivelling of the wheels to the left.

Intermediate wheel-swivelling resistance. When the road wheels offer less than their maximum resistance the frictional forces are reduced and the bell crank lever is moved through a smaller arc. The movement of the ball is less and the resulting build-up of pressure in the upper chamber is less. The difference between the two forces acting on the piston is therefore less and the power assistance is provided only to the extent that it is required. Power assistance is only provided after a certain torque has been exerted at the steering wheel, and only continues for as long as the steering wheel is being turned – the valve returning to its position of equilibrium the moment the wheel is still.

Maintenance

The system requires little attention. Only the top grades of the recommended fluids must be used. Absolute cleanliness is essential during topping up and overhaul operations. Drive-belt tension must be correct or low pressures will result. Pressure adjustments must only be made in accordance with the manufacturers' instructions.

The link or jack system (Figures 9.8 and 9.9)

Construction

In one such system the forward end of a double-walled cylinder is attached to (a) the lower end of the steering drop arm and (b) the

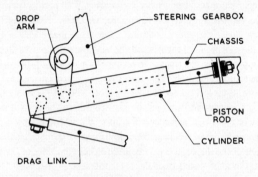

Fig. 9.8   Link type

forward end of the drag link. The cylinder encloses a spool type of control valve, and a piston and piston rod. The piston divides the cylinder to form inner and outer chambers, and the outer end of the piston rod is secured to the chassis by a flexible rubber mounting. The spool valve is moved inward (left) by a spring and outward (right) by the drop arm. The valve is automatically centralized when steering effort is not exerted.

Operation

When the spring moves the control spool inward it directs high-pressure fluid into the inner chamber, and allows fluid to escape from the outer chamber. The resulting pressure difference causes the cylinder to move over the piston away from the chassis – forcing the drag link to move in the same direction, but with greater force, than with the manual effort. When the drop arm moves the spool outward (right) high-pressure fluid enters the outer chamber. At the same time the fluid in the inner chamber is released, and the pressure difference causes the cylinder to move over the piston towards the chassis. This movement once again assists the manual effort, the power assistance ceasing as the spool centralizes when steering wheel motion ceases. Fluid escaping from the cylinder is returned to the reservoir.

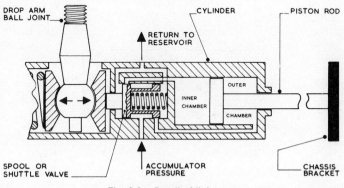

Fig. 9.9   Detail of link type

A very similar system can be operated by compressed air, and the power cylinder may be arranged transversely instead of longitudinally.

BRAKES

The efficiency of a properly maintained braking system is governed by the adhesion between the tyres and the road surface. The application of the brakes must retard the motion of the vehicle without causing it to veer to one side, or skid. A braked wheel exerts its maximum retardation just before its rotation is stopped. A wheel which stops (locks) while the vehicle is still moving exerts a greatly reduced retarding force and, which is possibly more important, causes skidding and loss of control. Locking usually occurs at the rear wheels – as a result of the reduced adhesion which occurs when weight is transferred from the rear wheels to the front wheels during retardation.

Pressure-limiting valve (Figure 9.10)

The possibility of rear wheel locking, and the associated skidding, can be minimized by the use of a pressure-limiting valve. This may replace the tee-junction in the pipe line to the rear brakes, and consists of a plunger and seat. The fluid passages through the valve are normally kept open by the action of the spring on the plunger so the same pressure acts in all of the brake cylinders. When pressures are applied

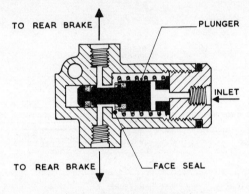

Fig. 9.10   Pressure-limiting valve

which exceed the loading of the spring the plunger is forced to move and close the passages through the valve. The pressure in the rear brake cylinders is therefore limited, and the higher pressure acts at the front brakes – where adhesion is increased as a result of the weight transfer.

Although pressure-limiting valves do help in the obtaining of better braking and vehicle handling they can only operate at one predetermined fluid pressure, i.e. they are not sensitive to the retardation of the vehicle and the adhesion of the rear wheels. One device which does respond to the rate of retardation is the Girling G valve.

Girling G valve (Figure 9.11)

This valve is fitted into the system immediately after the master cylinder and consists essentially of a steel ball which is free to move in a bore. The bore is inclined through an angle determined by the designers of the vehicle and braking system, and must not be altered. When the brakes are applied, inertia forces acting on the ball tend to cause it to

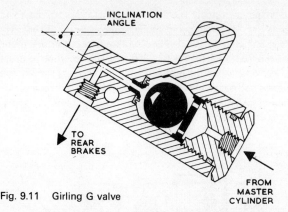

Fig. 9.11 Girling G valve

move up the inclined bore. When a predetermined *rate* of retardation occurs, the inertia forces are sufficiently large to force the ball to move up the inclined bore and close the port communicating with the rear brake cylinders – so limiting the pressure acting in them. Note that it is the *rate* of retardation which produces the limitation and not a predetermined pressure. The actual pressure will vary according to braking conditions, e.g. when travelling downhill the inclination of the bore will result in the valve closing at a lower pressure (earlier) and when travelling uphill at a higher pressure (later).

The valve may also include spring-loaded primary and differential pistons which are arranged in parallel with the G valve. When the brakes are first applied the same fluid pressure acts in all of the wheel cylinders. As the pressure is increased the primary piston is forced back to compress or load its spring, and the retardation of the vehicle results in the ball valve closing the rear brake port. Further pedal movement directly increases the pressure in the front brake cylinders and, by forcing the differential piston to move the primary piston outward, also increases the pressure in the rear brake cylinders – but at a lower rate because of the difference between the face areas of the two pistons. The initial loading of the spring of the primary piston ensures that the pressure changes in the rear brakes occur smoothly, and that the best possible ratios between the front and rear brakes are obtained.

Automatic adjusters (Figures 9.12 and 9.13)

These are intended to maintain the correct shoe-to-drum clearance automatically and are usually friction-and-ratchet types. In one front brake assembly of the leading-and-trailing-shoe type the shoes carry pins which are linked by a flat bar. The clearance between the pin of the trailing shoe and the hole in the bar is such that the correct shoe-to-drum clearance is provided when the brakes are off. The leading shoe end of the bar is slotted and has ratchet teeth on its lower edge. This end passes through friction pads which are loaded by a spring and nut on the pin, the pads being enclosed by a ratchet spring.

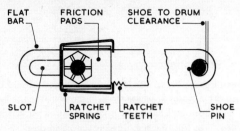

Fig. 9.12   Automatic adjuster (front)

When the brakes are applied the initial movement takes up the clearance, and then the bar is pulled through the friction pads. As these have sufficient grip to resist the shoe pull-off springs, the bar does not return to its original position when the brakes are released, i.e. the shoes

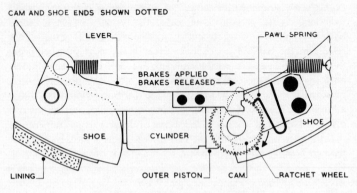

Fig. 9.13   Automatic adjuster (rear)

are adjusted. The ratchet device is a safeguard if the friction pads should lose their action due to oil or water, acting to hold the shoes in cruder adjustment due to the essential spacing of the teeth.

The leading shoe of the rear brake carries a ratchet and cam which rests against the outer piston. A ratchet wheel is attached to the adjusting cam, and a spring-loaded lever pawl and a pawl spring are engaged with the wheel.

When the brakes are applied the lever moves over the wheel. If no wear occurs at the linings the lever will return to its original position but if wear greater than normal shoe movement occurs the lever pawl will engage the next tooth on the wheel. As the brakes are released and the shoes move back, the lever pushes the wheel round by one tooth, turning the adjuster cam to compensate for the lining wear. The lift of the cam is less than the pitch of the ratchet-wheel teeth, so the correct clearance is obtained. The pawl spring prevents the lever pawl turning the wheel when the brakes are applied.

Brake servo units
Function
These units are used to obtain a more powerful retardation of the vehicle without the use of increased pedal force. They are fitted into the fluid system after the master cylinder, and use a pressure difference between the two sides of a vacuum piston to increase the pressure acting in the wheel cylinders. This pressure must always be directly proportional to the applied pedal force to enable the driver to feel his braking. Usually the pressure in the cylinders is between one and three times that provided by the master cylinder.

Principles
Direct or non-suspended type. In these both sides of the vacuum piston are normally subjected to atmospheric pressure, and one side is exhausted when the brakes are applied (manifold depression or exhauster unit).

Suspended vacuum type. In these both sides of the vacuum piston are normally subjected to depression (pressure less than atmospheric) and air at atmospheric pressure is introduced at one side when the brakes are applied. This method produces the more rapid response.

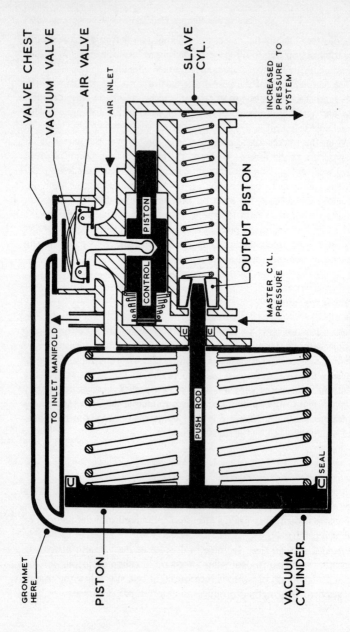

Fig. 9.14 Brake servo unit

Construction

Fig. 9.14 shows the essential components and their arrangement. Air is filtered before it enters the unit and a non-return valve is fitted at either the inlet manifold or the vacuum tank. The area of the larger end of the control piston is subjected to the fluid pressure of the master cylinder and the smaller end to the output pressure – the difference between these areas determining the ratio of master-cylinder pressure to servo-output pressure.

Operation

Brakes applied. The pedal force is converted into fluid pressure which acts equally in all the brake cylinders and on both ends of the control piston. As the two ends have different areas the piston is forced to move away from the vacuum cylinder and in so doing opens the air valve. This allows atmospheric pressure to act in the outer chamber of the vacuum cylinder and the pressure difference causes the vacuum piston and its attached push rod to move towards the slave cylinder. The push rod closes the conical hole in the output piston and forces it along its bore – so increasing the pressure in the brake cylinders and that operating on the smaller end of the control piston. Note that the brakes can be operated without servo assistance.

Brakes holding. The movement of the output piston, and the build-up of fluid pressure, continue until the piston takes up a neutral position where both valves are closed. This occurs when the *force* on the piston due to master-cylinder pressure acting on the large end is equalled by the *force* due to the higher output pressure acting on the small end. When both valves are held closed the brakes are held on. If the pedal force is then increased the control piston will be forced from its balanced position to reopen the air valve. The output pressure will then be increased until the piston reaches its balanced position or until the limit of available vacuum is reached.

Brakes released. When the pedal is released the pressure acting in the master cylinder, and on the large end of the control valve, suddenly collapses. The output pressure moves the control valve piston and opens the vacuum valve, the air valve remaining closed. The outer chamber of the vacuum cylinder is exhausted and, as the pressures at each side of the vacuum piston are the same, the piston is forced away from the slave cylinder by the spring. This action withdraws the push rod and fluid returns to the reservoir via the slave cylinder and the master cylinder.

NOTE. The piston of the vacuum cylinder has a return stop. This controls the clearance between the push rod and the output piston when the brakes are off. As this clearance governs the fluid flow when the brakes are first applied, and affects the smoothness of brake operation, it must not be altered during normal service.

Table 9.1　　Faults and causes

Fault	Cause	Remedy
Loss of fluid	Worn or damaged seals	Replace seals
	Scored bores	Replace unit
Hard pedal – little servo assistance	Inadequate depression Restricted hoses Blocked air inlet	Check or replace filter and hoses
	Damaged output piston Major fault in unit	Replace unit
Slow servo action	Restricted air inlet Swollen rubber grommet on vacuum pipe	Clear. Replace filter Replace grommet
Brakes not releasing	Vacuum piston out of alignment	Strip and re-align
	Vacuum piston stop not set correctly	Re-set
	Swollen rubber grommet	Replace
No assistance on heavy braking	Air leak into inner chamber of vacuum cylinder	Replace seals
Poor engine idling	Leaking vacuum hoses	Replace
	Damaged non-return valve at manifold or vacuum tank	Replace

Lockheed tandem master cylinder

Although the complete and sudden failure of a fluid brake system is rare it is not unknown. Tandem cylinders are one method of ensuring

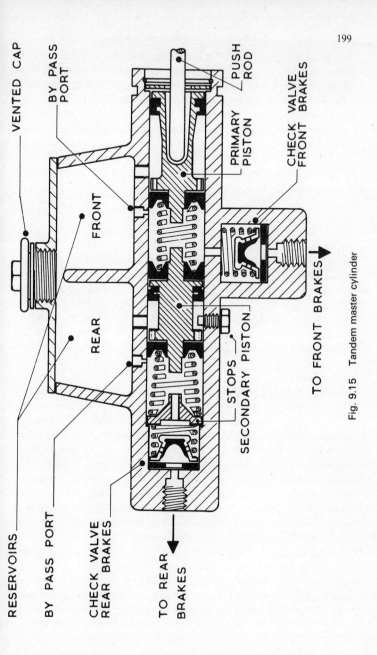

VENTED CAP

BY PASS PORT

RESERVOIRS

BY PASS PORT

CHECK VALVE REAR BRAKES

TO REAR BRAKES

FRONT

REAR

PUSH ROD

PRIMARY PISTON

CHECK VALVE FRONT BRAKES

TO FRONT BRAKES

STOPS

SECONDARY PISTON

Fig. 9.15   Tandem master cylinder

that in the event of a brake failure at least two wheels can be braked. These cylinders are larger, more complicated, and more expensive than the single types but ensure increased safety. They are fitted to the larger cars, and to some commercial vehicles. In effect they are two-piston assemblies fitted into one cylinder, the pressure produced by the movement of the rear piston operating the front brakes and simultaneously moving the forward piston – so producing an identical pressure to operate the rear brakes. (This same principle can be used to obtain a servo action if the pressure-powered piston is of larger diameter than the first piston.)

Construction

The unit is arranged as shown in Figure 9.15, the front and rear brake chambers each having their own reservoir. The primary piston is moved by the push rod and has a cylindrical stop on its pressure face. The secondary piston has stops at each end and a hollow piston stop is arranged in the end of the cylinder. The secondary piston also has a screwed stop which passes through the wall of the cylinder. The check valve assembly for the rear brakes is fitted into the end of the cylinder, a similar valve for the front brakes being fitted into the *side* of the cylinder near to the front brake chamber.

Operation

Normal. When the pedal is depressed the push rod forces the primary piston to move along the bore. Its seal covers the by-pass port and the fluid in the front brake chamber is totally enclosed. As this occurs the spring between the pistons moves the secondary piston and the fluid in the rear brake chamber is totally enclosed. Continued pedal movement results in pressure building up equally in both chambers, and when this exceeds the static line pressure both check valves are opened. The higher pressure is at once transmitted to the wheel cylinders and the brake shoes are applied to their drums. When the pedal is released the two pistons are returned by their springs and the normal recuperation action of the two chambers occurs simultaneously.

Rear brake system damaged. The primary piston is moved by the push rod in the normal manner but the pressure build-up results in the secondary piston forcing the fluid out of the damaged portion of the rear brake system. The pressure in the rear brake chamber collapses and that in the front brake chamber is reduced until the stop of the secondary piston contacts the stop in the end of the cylinder. Continued pedal movement then results in a pressure build-up in the front brake chamber and the operation of the front brakes. Note that the pedal movement is greatly increased.

Front brake system damaged. If this occurs the movement of the primary piston forces fluid out of the front brake system. Continued pedal movement results in the stop of the primary piston contacting the stop on the rear of the secondary piston – and the secondary piston is then moved directly to apply the rear brakes. Extra pedal movement occurs but some braking is still possible.

Bisector expander

These units are used where the brake shoes are forced outward through the action of a wedge and where both fluid and mechanical operation have to be provided for one shoe assembly. As the fluid cylinder is outside the brake drum, cooler operation is obtained and these units are commonly used in rear brakes of commercial vehicles.

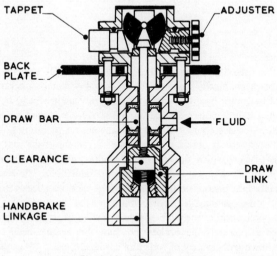

Fig. 9.16   Bisector expander

Construction (Figure 9.16)

The unit consists of two main assemblies: (a) the expander which has two tappets and either a wedge and rollers or a wedge and two rolling segments, and (b) the draw-bar mechanism for the wedge. The two assemblies are bolted together through the brake backplate and are free to slide to enable the shoes to centralize themselves in the drum.

Operation

By fluid pressure. The pressure in the piston chamber is increased as the brake pedal is depressed. The piston is forced to move outward and in turn forces the draw link and the attached draw bar to move away from the backplate. This action draws the wedge inward and forces the tappets out to apply the shoes to the drum. The handbrake linkage is unaffected because a clearance exists between the end of the handbrake rod and the inner end of the draw link, i.e. the draw link moves over the end of the handbrake rod.

By hand brake. The outward movement of the handbrake rod is transferred directly to the draw link and draw bar – so expanding the tappets. As the draw link is free from the piston, the piston does not move and the fluid system is unaffected by the operation of the handbrake.

Air brakes

These are used for many of the larger commercial vehicles. Any design of mechanically operated shoe assembly can be operated or powered by compressed air, and it may be convenient to also fit other units which can be powered by air under pressure, e.g. semi-automatic gearboxes, power steering rams, door mechanisms, or lifting hoists.

In compressed-air braking systems the movement of the foot pedal operates a valve which directs the air under pressure to pneumatic cylinders attached to, or near to, each shoe assembly. The resulting movement of the pistons or diaphragms in the cylinders, acting through rods and levers, causes the partial rotation of the shoe-operating cams and the application of the brakes. Additional air pipes and stop cocks are fitted to power trailer brakes. The hand brakes are mechanically operated through a system of rods and levers and usually act upon the rear brakes only.

System (Figures 9.17 and 9.18)

The system described is one used for eight-wheeled vehicles, operating the wheel assemblies of the foremost front axle only and all four of the rear wheel assemblies. The assemblies are of the two-shoe, mechanically expanded type.

The air system includes the following units:

(1) An air cleaner and silencer which may incorporate a de-icer.
(2) An air compresser which may be a single- or double-piston type, or a rotary-vane type.
(3) Control or non-return valves, and an unloader or diverter valve.
(4) A pressure tank or reservoir with a safety valve.
(5) A brake valve connected to the pedal.
(6) A system of steel and flexible pipes which connect the various units and include pipes to supply trailer brakes and emergency systems.
(7) Air-operated cylinders for each brake assembly.
(8) An air-pressure gauge mounted in the driver's cab.

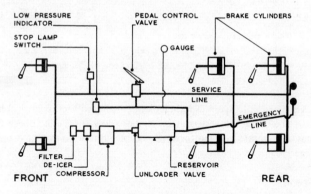

Fig. 9.17   Compressed-air brakes — tractor system

Arrangement

The air compressor is gear driven from the rear of the gearbox. The air cleaner and de-icer is fitted near the compressor and so arranged that it will not easily become choked by dirt. The reservoir is a strong steel tank, which can be charged by the compressor in about one and a half minutes, and which is mounted on the side of the chassis behind the cab. The unloader valve and the check or non-return valve are built into the same body, and this is mounted on the forward end of the reservoir. The check valve prevents the back flow of compressed air, and the unloader valve disconnects the reservoir when the pressure inside it reaches about $700 \, kN/m^2$. When the reservoir pressure falls, the unloader valve reconnects the supply of compressed air to the reservoir instead of directing it into the atmosphere. The reservoir is fitted with a safety valve which opens at a pressure just above 700

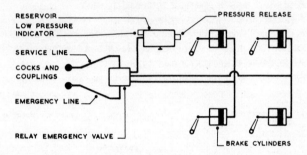

Fig. 9.18   Compressed air-brakes – trailer system

kN/m^2 and only operates if the unloader valve fails to operate properly – so protecting the system from excessive pressures. The brake valve may be mounted on the forward end of the reservoir or be a treadle type.

Operation
Brakes applied. When the pedal is depressed the brake valve directs air, at a pressure proportional to the applied pedal force, into the brake-operating cylinders. The cylinder pistons or diaphragms are forced outward and turn the shoe-actuating cams to force the shoes to contact the drums.
Brakes released. When the pedal is released the air pressure in the system is exhausted through the brake valve. The cylinder pistons or diaphragms are returned by their springs as the brake shoe pull-off springs retract the shoes.

Table 9.2   Fault diagnosis

Fault	Causes	Remedies
Slow pressure build-up	Blocked air filter	Clean or replace
	Pipe leaking between compressor and reservoir reservoir and gauge or trailer couplings	Test for leaks and correct faults
	Unloader valve not seating correctly	Strip and check valve – refit
	Leaks at brake valve, drain cocks, or charging connection	Replace or overhaul
	Compressor weak	Overhaul valves and springs
Compressor not unloading	Unloader valve not completely closing	Overhaul
Pressure not held	Check valve not seating	Overhaul unloader and check valve unit
	Leaks in system	Check at all points – correct faults found
Slow brake application	Lining or drums worn excessively or need adjustment	Replace or readjust
	Brake valve sticking	Strip and clean
	Low pressure in line	Adjust pedal stops
	Partly blocked pipes	Clear or replace
	Leaking pipes	Locate and repair
Brakes stay on	Brake camshafts binding	Free and lubricate
	Inadequate shoe clearance	Readjust
	Brake valve not fully returning	Check return spring and pedal off-stop
	Brake valve sticking or not sealing	Strip and clean – check valve and seat condition
Fierce brakes	Pedal adjustment faulty	Check pedal on-stop
	Brake valve sticking	Strip and clean

Continuous-flow hydraulic system (Figure 9.19)

The continuous flow systems offer, at less cost, the same advantages as the compressed-air systems, i.e. the convenience of being able to

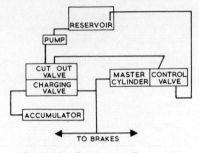

Fig. 9.19   Continuous-flow system

power other units such as door rams, steering rams, and tipper rams from the same power source.

Construction (Figure 9.20)

The basic components of the system are:

(1) A two-compartment reservoir.
(2) A multi-plunger radial pump.
(3) A combined cut-out and charging valve.
(4) A pressure accumulator.
(5) A combined master cylinder and control valve.

The reservoir has separate inner and outer compartments which are connected respectively to the master cylinder and the hydraulic pump. The outlet to the pump is protected by a cylindrical filter. One fluid system powers the master cylinder of the other system.

The multi-plunger radial pump is driven from either the engine or the gearbox and delivers fluid to the cut-out and charging valve unit. Note that the pump only circulates fluid – it does not produce pressure on the fluid until the circulation is obstructed by the movement of the brake pedal. When this occurs, pressures of between 5520 kN/m^2 and 8280 kN/m^2 are built up at once, the actual pressure being determined by the applied pedal force. The cut-out valve directs high-pressure fluid into the accumulator and, when the accumulator is fully charged, into

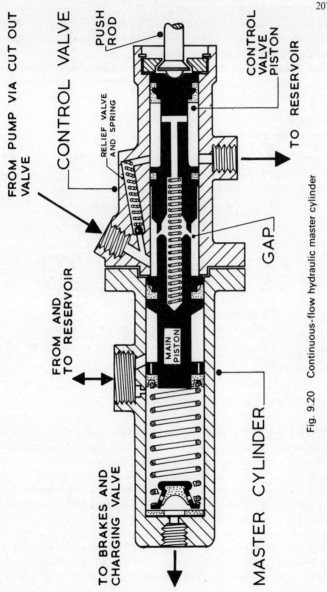

FROM PUMP VIA CUT OUT VALVE

CONTROL VALVE

PUSH ROD

CONTROL VALVE PISTON

RELIEF VALVE AND SPRING

TO RESERVOIR

FROM AND TO RESERVOIR

GAP

MAIN PISTON

TO BRAKES AND CHARGING VALVE

MASTER CYLINDER

Fig. 9.20   Continuous-flow hydraulic master cylinder

the annular space between the faces of the main master-cylinder piston and the control-valve piston. When the brakes are not applied the fluid (no pressure) returns to the outer compartment of the reservoir from this space. The charging valve releases fluid under pressure from the accumulator into the circuit whenever the pump delivery is insufficient to provide full servo operation. Fig. 9.21 shows the valve assembly.

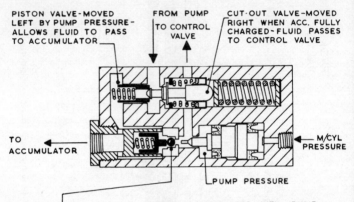

Fig. 9.21 Valve assembly

Where the system is used only to power the brakes, the accumulator consists of a spring-loaded piston enclosed by a strong cylindrical case. Where additional systems are also hydraulically powered the accumulator has to be much larger. These types consist of a strong cylindrical case which encloses a reinforced rubber bag. The bag is filled with air or nitrogen at a pressure of 3450 kN/m^2 and when this is fully compressed by the fluid the pressure in the accumulator is the same as the normal pressure in the circuit. The bag requires topping up at intervals and its action is similar to that of a spring – the stored energy being released in delivering high-pressure fluid into the circuit as required.

The master cylinder and control valve may be either barrel or integral tank types. In both, normal master-cylinder operation occurs, but the main piston is operated by the fluid pressure provided by the pump.

Operation

Brakes off. In this condition fluid is circulating through the units and returning to the outer compartment of the reservoir (no pressure). The accumulator is fully charged with fluid under normal working pressure.

Brakes applied. As the pedal is depressed its push rod forces the piston of the control valve to move inward. This movement reduces the size of the gap maintained between the control piston and the main piston and so obstructs the flow of fluid through the circuit. The pump forces the fluid to flow and a pressure of between 5520 kN/m^2 and 8280 kN/m^2 is immediately built up. The actual pressure is directly proportional to the reduction in the size of the gap, i.e. to the applied pedal force. This pressure acts in the annular space between the two pistons and forces the main piston to increase the pressure in the master cylinder and the wheel cylinders – so applying the brakes. This pressure, by also acting on the face of the control-valve piston, resists the movement of the pedal and allows the driver to feel his braking. The face area of the main piston is much larger than that of the control-valve piston but both are subjected to the same pressures. This results in a much greater *force* being applied to the main piston, the ratio of the two forces being determined by the ratio of the two face areas, i.e. if the face area ratio is $3:1$ then a pressure of 1400 kN/m^2 on the control piston will produce a pressure of 4200 kN/m^2 at the main piston to operate the brakes.

Brakes released. When the pedal is released, the control and main pistons are returned to their stops by their springs. The maximum gap between the two is restored and as this occurs the pressure in the fluid circuit collapses and normal circulation is resumed. In the brake system the fluid returns to the master cylinder, the cylinder is recuperated in the normal way, and the excess fluid is returned to the inner compartment of the reservoir.

NOTE. The brakes can be operated without servo assistance, the control piston moving the main master-cylinder piston directly. A pressure gauge or warning lamp is mounted in the cab to provide warning of no pressure or too-low pressure. When bleeding is necessary, each unit in sequence is bled. The brake system is bled in the normal manner.

Table 9.3   Fault diagnosis

Fault	Causes	Remedies
Pressure not indicated by gauge or lamp	Gauge defective	Replace
	Short in lamp circuit	Locate and repair
	Reservoir empty or filter choked	Top up or clean
	Air leak into pump feed pipe line	Locate, repair or replace
	Pump drive sheared or pump defective	Replace
Gauge fluctuates	Cut-out valve chattering due to (a) damaged bag in accumulator or (b) leak through cut-out or valves	(a) Replace bag (b) Clean or replace
Slow charging by pump	Air leak into pump feed pipe	Locate and repair
	Pump not vented	Bleed
	Damaged valve stem or seat – cut-out valve	Replace valve or unit
	Damaged ball in charging valve	Replace valve or unit
Fluid discharge from reservoir	Excess of fluid due to topping up without first releasing pressure in accumulator	Release pressure and top up again
Pressure falls to nil as brakes applied	Accumulator bag air pressure collapsed	Recharge or replace
	Master-cylinder seals, valve seats, or relief valve worn or damaged	Replace
Steady pressure loss as brakes applied	Master-cylinder seals, valve seats, or relief valve worn or damaged	Replace
Steady pressure loss when pump not running	Accumulator bag or inflation valve leaking	Repair or replace
	Leakage at cut-out or charging valves	Clean or replace

Fault	Causes	Remedies
Noise from pump	Fluid level too low	Top up
	Filter blocked	Clean or replace
	Air leak into pump feed pipe	Locate and repair
	Pump not vented	Bleed
	Bleed screw leaking	Tighten or replace
	Mechanical damage in pump	Replace unit

NOTE. The pressure accumulator must be discharged and drained before any part of the system is disconnected.

Auxiliary brakes
These are powerful and smooth, and usually operate through the transmission system. They may be put into operation by either a small lever under the steering wheel or a small pedal above the main brake pedal. Auxiliary brakes are particularly useful in hilly or mountainous districts where their use (instead of the main brakes) allows the main brakes to be kept cool and efficient ready for emergency use, i.e. to avoid brake fade as a result of overheating when travelling down long gradients.

The use of auxiliary brakes can result in savings of about 30% of brake-lining wear, together with reduced tyre wear and less driver fatigue. It is also claimed that, as the road wheels cannot be locked by these brakes, the handling of the vehicle on wet and very slippery surfaces is greatly improved.

Exhaust brakes (Figure 9.22)
These operate through the transmission system by using the engine as a low-pressure air compressor, i.e. restricting the passage of gases from the engine. The exhaust brake consists of a malleable iron valve arranged in a cylindrical bore, of larger diameter than the exhaust pipe, fitted into the exhaust system near the exhaust manifold. The valve has stops which limit its travel such that the pressure build-up does not exceed about $310 \, kN/m^2$. The valve is moved by a compressed-air or

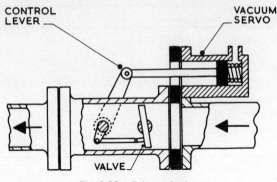

Fig. 9.22   Exhaust brake

vacuum servo, or by an electrical solenoid. The control device is inter-connected with the fuel cut-off device of the C.I. injection pump, so fuel economy is also improved by the use of this type of brake.

One disadvantage of the exhaust brake is that it cannot be used on a vehicle fitted with a two-stroke C.I. engine. A less important feature is that air cleaners of the oil-bath type cannot be used because the oil would be blown out.

NOTE. The setting of the valve stops in installation is critical and must be carried out according to the instructions of the engine manufacturer.

Eddy-current brakes (Figure 9.23)
In one type, twin air-cooled, disc-shaped rotors are connected into the transmission between the gearbox and the propeller shaft. These rotors are supported and located by taper roller bearings fitted inside a stator unit arranged between the two rotors. The stator unit is supported in the chassis by flexible mountings, and has a number of electromagnets with pole pieces arranged around its circumference. When battery voltage energizes the magnets, their magnetic fields are concentrated by the pole pieces and pass through the moving rotors. The resulting eddy currents exert strong retarding forces on the rotors and therefore upon the transmission.

The electromagnets, or poles, are connected in groups, each having its own circuit. The circuits are brought into action as the control lever is moved – so providing a steadily increasing retardation. If one circuit fails, the others still operate. The normal stop lamps, and a lamp in the

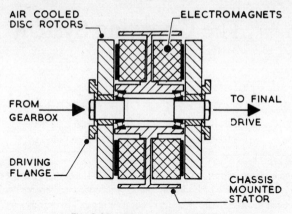

Fig. 9.23   Eddy-current brakes

cab, light up when these brakes are applied. Fairly heavy but not excessive currents are required, and these brakes can be incorporated into the normal 12-V or 24-V systems.

10

The Charging System

Function

The generator, or dynamo, is used to maintain the state of charge of the battery. It converts mechanical energy into electrical energy which is then used to reverse the chemical action of the cell materials – so maintaining an adequate potential difference between the terminal posts of the battery.

Principle

The construction of a generator is, in principle, very similar to that of the motor, but generator action is the reverse of motor action.

When a wire loop is made to rotate in a magnetic field a voltage is induced in the loop as it cuts across the field. If the ends of the loop are connected to an external circuit by brushes and slip rings the voltage so induced will cause a current to flow around the external circuit. The voltage will vary in strength as the loop rotates, rising to a maximum as the loop passes through the strongest part of the field (loop on field axis) and returning to zero as the loop passes through the weakest part of the field (loop at right angle to field axis). The induced voltage also varies with the strength of the magnetic field, the speed at which the loop cuts across the field, and the length of the loop.

In 360° of rotation the loop is turned over twice, causing the direction of the current to be changed every 180° of rotation. The output of this type of generator is therefore alternating current (a.c.) and as the current flows in one direction its voltage rises and falls, and then rises and falls again as the direction of the current is reversed. This voltage variation can be illustrated by a wave diagram which shows the rise and fall of the voltage about a neutral axis as the loop is rotated. The *peak* voltages above the axis represent positive current and those below the axis represent negative current direction.

Commutation

Because alternating current cannot be used to charge batteries or operate solenoids, the current induced in the loop has to be made to flow in one direction only, i.e. has to be converted into direct current (d.c.) – see Fig. 10.1. This conversion, or rectification, can be made by the use of a commutator which replaces the slip rings.

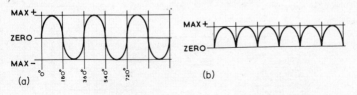

(a)

(b)

Fig. 10.1*a*   Alternating current   Fig. 10.1*b*   Direct current –
                                                              full-wave rectification

In practical generators, a large number of loops or coils are used, the ends of each loop being soldered to adjacent segments on the commutator and the beginning of one loop being soldered to the same segment as the end of the previous loop. This overlapping of the loops is called 'lap' winding. By employing a large number of loops a large number of maximum voltages are induced. The commutator, by acting as a rotary switch, reverses the loop connections at the correct moment and ensures that all the voltages are positive. The resulting output is direct current at a steady voltage – which is suitable for battery charging.

Construction

The main components of the practical generator (see Fig. 10.2) are the rotating armature and the case or yoke. The armature consists of a steel shaft upon which are mounted a drive pulley; a laminated, cylindrical soft-iron core; and a copper and micanite commutator. The armature loops or coils are fitted into slots arranged around the armature core. Two field coils with magnetized soft-iron polepieces are secured to the inside of the cylindrical soft-iron yoke by large counter-sunk screws.

The core of the armature rotates in close proximity to the shaped polepieces, the magnetic field flowing from one to the other via the armature core. The magnetic circuit is completed via the yoke. The driven end of the armature shaft is supported and located by a ball bearing arranged in the drive end-plate or bracket. The opposite end of the shaft is supported by a plain, sintered bronze bush in the rear-end bracket. This bracket also carries the spring-loaded carbon commutator brushes. One of the two brushes is earthed via the end bracket while the other brush is insulated from the bracket and connected to the output terminal (marked D).

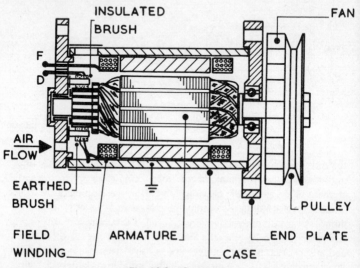

Fig. 10.2   Generator

The complete assembly of the armature, yoke, and brackets is held together by long bolts which pass through the drive plate and are screwed into the end-plate. Both brackets are slotted to allow a fan, attached to the drive pulley, to draw a stream of air through the unit to cool the commutator and the armature loops or coils. The air enters through the rear bracket and leaves through the drive end bracket. Ventilated generators are able to provide higher output currents – without damage – than sealed types.

The field coils are used to increase the strength of the magnetic field and are wound to produce opposite polarities, i.e. they become electromagnets when current is passed through them. Generators for the larger vehicles may have four field coils but the majority of generators have only two. These are connected to each other in series and are

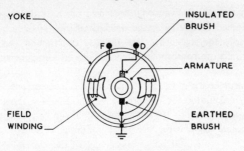

Fig. 10.3   Shunt generator

arranged in parallel with the armature coils. One end of the field-coil combination is connected to earth via the yoke and the other end is connected to the field terminal (F) on the rear bracket. See Fig. 10.3.

When the terminals D and F are connected (by the action of the

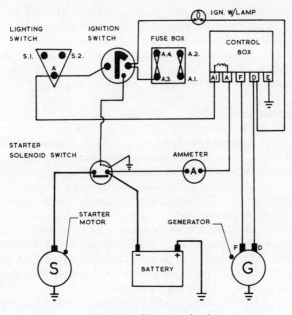

Fig. 10.4   Charging circuit

regulator), the current induced in the armature coils also flows through the field coils. This increases the strength of the magnetic field and so also increases the strength of the induced current, i.e. the faster the speed of armature rotation the stronger the field and the stronger the output current.

This characteristic of the shunt (parallel) connected generator makes it *by itself* unsuitable for use on the vehicle. Vehicle generators may rotate at speeds of up to 10 000 rev/min, and at these speeds the output voltage would destroy the electrical equipment. At low speeds the generator voltage would be less than that of the battery. The vehicle generator is therefore operated in conjunction with a control box which incorporates an output regulator and an automatic cut-out. See Fig. 10.4.

THE CONTROL BOX

Voltage control (regulator)

Generator output is obtained when the terminals D and F are connected. When they are disconnected the field circuit is broken and the output is reduced because the strength of the magnetic field is reduced. Control of the generator output can therefore be obtained by the use of a switch which automatically makes and breaks the connection between D and F. This switch is the voltage regulator.

Construction (Figure 10.5)

The base of the control unit is a U-shaped iron core or yoke upon which are mounted the iron cores of the regulator and cut-out bobbins. An adjustable tungsten contact is arranged above the regulator bobbin and is insulated from the yoke. A second tungsten contact is mounted on an L-shaped armature arranged between the bobbin and the adjustable contact. This armature is suspended from the side of the yoke by a spring blade and a lower spring blade, loaded by an adjusting screw, forces the armature contact towards the adjustable contact.

The yoke is connected to terminal D of the generator, while the insulated adjustable contact is connected to terminal F. A coil is wound around the regulator bobbin, one end being connected to the yoke (D) and the other end to earth (terminal E on the control box). As this coil is arranged in parallel with the armature of the generator, it is known as the shunt coil.

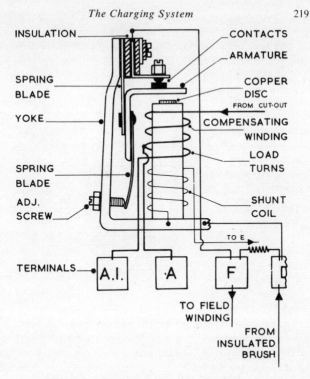

Fig. 10.5   Compensated voltage regulator

Operation (Figure 10.6)

The contacts are held closed by the lower spring blade, so joining terminals D and F. As the armature of the generator is rotated the induced voltage rises and current flows through the shunt coil to earth. The bobbin becomes an electromagnet and separates the contacts by attracting the armature to its core. Contact between the armature and the core is prevented by a copper disc.

As the contacts separate the generator output falls, the spring blade closes the contacts, and the output builds up again – the contacts opening and closing between 40 and 60 times per second. The movement of the armature is determined by the opposing effects upon it of the spring blade and the strength of the electromagnet, i.e. the output voltage. The output voltage of the generator is therefore limited to a preset value decided by the tension of the spring blade – irrespective of generator armature speed. This system is known as the constant-voltage control system.

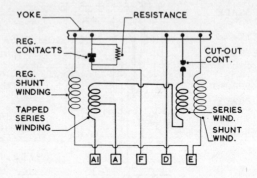

Fig. 10.6   Circuit for compensated voltage-control box

Points resistance. This is arranged in parallel with the contacts (between D and F) to prevent arcing when the contacts open while heavy currents are flowing between them. It provides an alternative path for the current while the contacts are opened and is short-circuited while they are closed.

Cut-out

When the engine is stopped, or is only running slowly, the output voltage of the generator is less than the terminal voltage of the battery. If not prevented, this would result in the battery discharging itself through the armature coils of the generator – which would then try to act as a motor. As the free self-rotation of the armature is prevented by the drive belt the armature would be rapidly destroyed by overheating, the excessive heat burning the insulation of the coils and melting the soldered connections of the armature.

This damage is prevented by the use of the cut-out, an automatic switch which disconnects the charging circuit from the battery when the output voltage of the generator falls below battery voltages, and reconnects it when the generator voltage exceeds battery voltage. The cut-out is also known as a reverse-current relay.

Construction (Figure 10.7)

The iron core of the cut-out bobbin is mounted upon the yoke of the control box, near the regulator, and a specially shaped armature is arranged over the bobbin. The armature is suspended from the side of the yoke by a spring blade, a lower blade with adjustable tension forcing the armature away from the core of the bobbin. A silver contact is fitted to the armature opposite a fixed silver contact which is insulated from the yoke. Note that the contacts are separated when generator voltage is less than battery voltage.

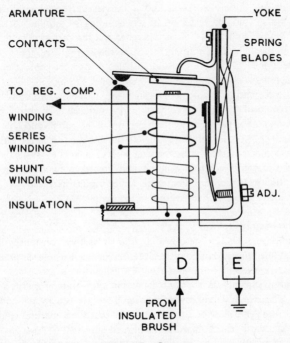

Fig. 10.7   Cut-out

The bobbin has two windings. The first (shunt) winding is connected in parallel with terminals D and E. This winding consists of a large number of turns of fine, insulated wire and it has a fairly high resistance, so it carries little or no current. It is sometimes called the no-load coil. The second (series or current) winding has only a few turns of heavy, insulated wire and is connected between the insulated contact and terminal A of the control box.

Operation

When the generator produces voltage, a small current flows from D to earth via the shunt winding, causing the bobbin to act as an electro-magnet. As the voltage rises to a preset value (determined by the tension of the spring blade) the electromagnet becomes strong enough to attract the armature against the action of the spring blade. The contacts are therefore closed and a heavier current flows through the contacts and the series or current winding to terminal A of the control box – and thence to the ammeter and the battery. The flow of current through this winding increases the strength of the electro-magnetic field of the bobbin and so helps to prevent contact chatter as the contacts close.

When the output voltage of the generator falls below battery voltage, the strength of the electromagnetic field is reduced. The spring blade now forces the armature away from the core of the bobbin and separates the contacts – so disconnecting the charging system from the battery. As the contacts separate a momentary flow of current from the battery passes through the series winding and creates a magnetic field in opposition to the existing field. This action results in a faster collapse of the field and a faster separation of the contacts.

Constant-voltage control

The voltage regulator described is known as the 'constant-voltage' type. While this appears to meet all requirements it would, in practice, have to be used in conjunction with a generator of excessively high generating capacity. When the battery is in a low state of charge a very large difference in voltage exists between it and the generator – and this would result in a flow of current so heavy that the armature windings of the standard generator would be burned out.

The constant-voltage regulator is therefore modified by adding another winding to the regulator bobbin, the system then being known as the 'compensated voltage-control' system.

Compensated voltage control (Figure 10.8)

In this system the difference between the battery and the generator output voltages is never allowed to become so great that excessively heavy currents can flow through the armature windings of the generator and the charging circuit. Excessive voltage differences are avoided by automatically altering the setting of the regulator so that output voltage varies according to the current passing through the battery.

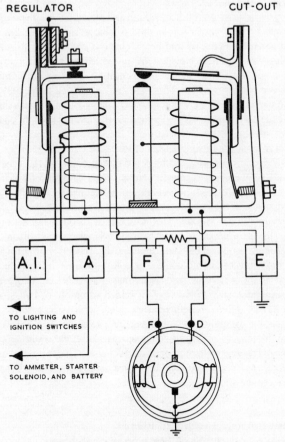

Fig. 10.8   Compensated voltage control

Compensating winding. The additional (compensating) winding on the regulator bobbin is in series with the series or current winding of the cut-out, and so carries the current flowing to the battery. The winding is so arranged that its magnetic field assists the field of the shunt coil in attracting the armature and separating the contacts, i.e. the heavier the flow of current the sooner the contacts are opened. The voltage is therefore regulated by the flow of current and excessively heavy currents are prevented.

Load turns or winding. If a heavy lamp and auxiliaries load was applied when the battery was in a low state of charge the voltage difference would again be increased and heavy currents would flow through the charging circuit. These currents are prevented by a small number of turns which are added to the compensating winding but connected at one end to terminal A.1. These are known as 'load turns' and act in the same manner as the compensating winding – but only when lamp or other external circuit loads are applied. Both windings keep the charging current within limits which protect the armature windings of the generator from the heating effects of excessive currents.

NOTE. The compensating windings are designed to suit the generator, and the load windings to suit the external electrical units of a particular vehicle. Control boxes and generators must only be interchanged in accordance with the recommendations of the manufacturer.

Temperature compensation. This is obtained through the action of a bi-metallic strip which is fitted behind the lower spring blade of the regulator armature. This strip enables the generator to provide an extra high rate of charge while it is cold – the rate being reduced to normal as the generator reaches its maximum working temperature. The bi-metallic strip consists of a welded assembly of two strips of metal having different coefficients of expansion. As their temperature increases the different rates of expansion cause the strip to bend and reduce the tension of the adjusting spring blade, the resulting output voltage decreasing as the temperature increases. This form of temperature compensating device is used in most *voltage* regulators but not in current regulators.

Compensated voltage-control adjustments

The service requirements of these types of control box usually consists of checking the electrical and mechanical settings, and cleaning the contacts. Note that the figures given in the following operational sequences are intended only as a guide. Always refer to the manufacturers' specifications for actual values relating to a particular unit.

Electrical settings

1. Output voltage on open circuit

Ensure that a good earth connection exists between the chassis and terminal E of the control box. The battery is disconnected from the generator by removing the A and A.1. cables from the control-box terminals. This also removes from the circuit the load winding of the regulator, so that only the shunt coil is in operation, and a more accurate setting is possible. The removed cables must be joined together to supply the ignition coil and enable the engine to be run.

Connect a voltmeter between earth and terminal D, with the red lead to earth and the black lead to D. Run the engine at charging speed (about 3000 rev/min) when the voltage should be limited between 16 and 16·5 V. If this is not so, the adjusting screw of the regulator armature must be turned to vary the tension on the spring blade – increasing the tension and the voltage by clockwise rotation and reducing the tension and the voltage by anticlockwise rotation. These adjustments should be carried out as quickly as possible to avoid overheating the shunt coil.

A very poor earth connection, a short between D and F, and an open-circuited shunt winding will result in the adjusting screw not altering the voltage to correct the regulation.

2. Cutting-in-voltage

With the voltmeter still in position connect an ammeter between the joint of the connected A and A.1. cables and the control-box terminal A. Switch on the headlamps and increase the engine speed. The voltmeter reading should increase and then drop slightly (as the cut-out contacts close) at between 12·75 V and 13·25 V. If this does not occur, the cut-out adjusting screw must be used to alter the tension of its armature spring blade.

The ammeter reading should increase also, moving from discharge to charge, as the speed of the generator is increased. As the speed is reduced it will indicate a discharge reading which should not exceed 3 A to 5 A before the cut-out contacts open. When the point of opening occurs the reading should be zero.

3. Contact cleaning

(a) Regulator. The regulator contacts are made of tungsten and should be cleaned with the aid of a carborundum stone or silicon-carbide paper.

(b) Cut-out. These contacts are made of silver and should only be cleaned with the aid of very fine glass paper.

Dust should be removed with the aid of a non-fluffy cloth moistened with methylated spirits.

4. Air gap setting

(a) Regulator. Slacken the screws securing the fixed contact plate to the yoke and the contact locknut. Place a feeler gauge of 0·021 in (0·53 mm) between the bobbin core and the armature and press the armature down upon the gauge. Tighten the screws. Screw in the contact until it touches the armature contact. Tighten the locknut. Remove the gauge and readjust the voltage as previously described.

(b) Cut-out. Slacken the screws, press the armature down to the core, and tighten the screws. By bending the stop arm, set a clearance between the arm and the armature tongue of 0·63 mm to 1·02 mm. Bend the arm of the insulated contact to give a follow-through contact of 0·229 mm to 0·585 mm.

Table 10.1   Checking the system

Check	Result obtained	Conclusion	Remedy
1. *Battery* – state of charge – hydrometer	Reading above 1·190	State of charge satisfactory	
	Reading below 1·190	State not satisfactory	Recharge by external charger
2. *Battery* – for condition – high rate discharge tester	Reading 1·5 V steady for 10 seconds	Condition satisfactory	
	Reading falls rapidly	Condition not satisfactory	Replace by new fully charged unit
3. *Fan belt* (a) Condition	Not bottoming in pulley No cracks	Condition satisfactory	
	Cracked or bottoming	Belt or/and pulley worn	Replace and re-tension
(b) Tension	0·5–0·75 in (13–19 mm) deflection longest side	Tension correct	
	More or less deflection	Tension incorrect	Readjust to correct tension
(c) Bearing condition	Little or no side movement	Bearings satisfactory	
	Excessive side movement	Bearings excessively worn	Replace

Table 10.1   Checking the system

Check	Result obtained	Conclusion	Remedy
4. *Generator* (a) Armature – Remove cables and connect voltmeter between D and a good earth. (Red lead to earth in positive earth system – black in negative earth system.) Run engine at 1200–1500 rev/min.	Voltmeter reads 1·5 V to 3·0 V	Brush gear and armature windings satisfactory	
	Reading increases with speed increase	Internal short between D and F	Examine field connections and rectify faults located
5. (b) Field circuit – voltmeter as in check 4. Connect ammeter between D and F terminals. Increase speed until voltmeter shows system voltage	Ammeter shows not more than 2 A	Field circuit satisfactory – generator satisfactory	
	Ammeter indicates much more than 2 A	Internal short circuit or earthed field coils	Strip unit, locate, repair fault, reassemble and test
6. *Cables* – reconnect at generator and remove from control box. Repeat checks 4.(a) and 4.(b) with meters connected to box end of cables. *Do not cross connections or the contacts and armature may be burned out*	Voltmeter reads as in 4	Cables satisfactory	Replace. Check. Remove instruments and refit cables
	Readings different from 4	Cables not satisfactory	
7. *Regulator* – voltage setting Remove A and A.1. cables and joint ends. Connect voltmeter between D terminal and earth. Run generator at 3000 rev/min.	Regulation occurs at 16 to 16·5 V	Voltage setting is correct	
	Regulation occurs at any other voltage	Setting is incorrect	Adjust tension of spring blade until correct reading obtained. If too low and will not adjust, clean contacts – if these burned, check D and F cables for reversal and resistance for condition. If too high and will not adjust, check earth connection and for short between D and F

Check	Result obtained	Conclusion	Remedy
8. *Cut-out* – cutting in voltage Voltmeter as in check 6. Connect ammeter between terminal A and joint of A and A.1. cables. Switch on headlamps and increase speed	Voltmeter reading falls slightly at 12·75 V to 13·25 V	Cutting in voltage satisfactory	Readjust cut-out spring blade tension. Remove instruments and reconnect cables
	Reading falls at any other voltage	Cutting in voltage incorrect	
9. *Charge current* – meters as above. Speed up generator	Ammeter reading increases as speed is increased	Circuit is satisfactory	
10. *Reverse current* – meters as above. Reduce speed steadily	Ammeter reading falls to indicate discharge – returns to zero between 3 A and 5 A discharge	Reverse current satisfactory	
11. *Volt drop* – supply line. Remove D cable from generator and insert ammeter into circuit. Connect voltmeter between D terminal and battery −ve (positive earth system) or +ve (negative earth system). Increase speed until ammeter shows 10 A	Voltmeter reading not more than 0·75 V	Volt drop normal	All units and connections are satisfactory

Current voltage control (Figure 10.10)

Although the compensated voltage control system has been successful for a number of years, a point has been reached where it can no longer meet the demands being made of it. The increased use of more and more electrically powered units in vehicle design has led to improved types of battery, generator, and control units. The current–voltage control system is an improvement over the compensated voltage system (see Fig. 10.9) and the alternator is an improvement over the generator as it has been for many years.

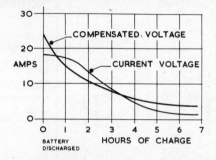

Fig. 10.9   Graph showing relative charge rates for compensated voltage control and current–voltage control

The current–voltage control system allows the generator to deliver its maximum output for a longer period at the beginning of the charge. The graph shows the difference between the charge rates of the two systems. In the compensated voltage system the charge starts at a fairly high rate but is reduced very quickly as battery voltage rises. In the current–voltage system a slightly lower rate of charge is maintained over a much longer period before being reduced to a lesser rate of trickle charge, i.e. the battery receives more charge in a given time.

Control-box construction

The control box of the current–voltage system consists of a cut-out, a voltage regulator, and a current regulator. Each of these has its own yoke, contacts, and adjusting device, and their construction and operation are similar to those described previously. The current regulator has no temperature compensation. It allows the generator to deliver its maximum output until the voltage of the system reaches a pre-set value. At this point it ceases to operate and the voltage regulator exerts control, gradually reducing the output voltage until only a trickle charge is passed through the battery. The three terminals are marked B, F, and D. B is connected to the battery via the ammeter, F is connected to F on the generator (field winding) and D is connected to D on the generator (armature brush).

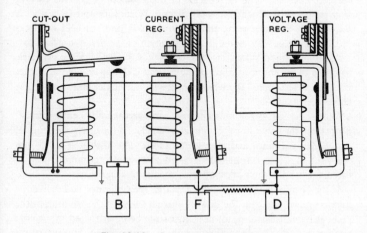

Fig. 10.10   Current–voltage control

Internal Circuit. Terminal D is connected to the yoke of the voltage regulator, and to one end of the shunt windings of the voltage regulator and the cut-out, the other ends of these windings being earthed. Terminal D is also connected to the heavy-gauge wire windings of the current regulator and cut-out and, via the yoke and contacts of the cut-out, to terminal B. A resistance is arranged between terminals D and F to reduce arcing at the contacts of the voltage regulator. A small winding at the top of this regulator (connected between the insulated contacts of the two regulators) assists the shunt winding of the voltage regulator and so makes possible a quicker opening of the contacts, i.e. increases the frequency of contact vibration. This winding is known as the bucking coil or the frequency coil. Note that when the generator is not in operation the contacts of both the current and the voltage regulator are closed but those of the cut-out are open.

System operation

As the armature of the generator is rotated a voltage is induced in its windings. As D and F are connected by the closed contacts current passes through the generator and control-box terminals D to the shunt windings of the voltage regulator and cut-out and to earth – producing magnetic fields which attract the armatures against the tension of the spring blades and tend to separate or open the contacts. This current also passes through the contacts of both regulators and to earth via the yoke of the current regulator, terminals F, and the field windings of the generator – so increasing the strength of the generator field and the output voltage. When this voltage reaches about 12·7 V the magnetic field due to the shunt winding of the cut-out is strong enough to attract the armature, against the tension of the spring blade, and to close the contacts.

When the cut-out contacts close, an increasingly heavy current flows from the generator through terminal D, and the heavy windings of the current regulator and the cut-out, to the yoke of the cut-out. From the yoke it passes through the cut-out contacts to terminal B and to earth via the ammeter and battery – so charging the battery.

If the battery is in a low state of charge the generator will deliver its maximum output, and the flow of current through the winding of the current regulator will result in its armature being attracted to the core against its spring blade and in its contacts being opened. This interrupts the flow of current through the generator field windings and therefore reduces its output. As the output is reduced the spring blade is enabled to close the contacts and the output is increased. These contacts, by opening and closing (vibrating) at between 60 and 100 times per second, effectively limit the output of the generator to its safe maximum current.

As the battery voltage increases, the voltage in the system between it and the generator (line voltage) also increases, and when the battery is about one-third fully charged the line voltage will reach the voltage set by the adjustment of the voltage regulator. At this point the field of the voltage regulator shunt winding is able to attract its armature and open the contacts. These contacts commence to vibrate and so reduce the output voltage of the generator by reducing the strength of its field – vibrating at faster rates as the battery voltage increases until the battery receives only a trickle charge.

When the voltage regulator starts operating the flow of current through the winding of the current regulator is reduced so much that its magnetic field cannot hold the armature against the spring blade. Its contacts therefore remain closed and the current regulator ceases to operate.

The switching off of the engine will result in the voltage of the battery being higher than that of the generator. The reduction in the strength of the magnetic field of the cut-out shunt winding will enable the spring blade to open the contacts and isolate the charging circuit from the battery. This action is greatly assisted by a short-lived flow of battery current through the contacts and the heavy winding. As this current flows in the reverse from normal direction its field opposes and neutralizes the existing field and results in a faster and more positive opening of the cut-out contacts.

Current–voltage system checks
The tests for condition and satisfactory operation of the battery, the generator, and the circuit are the same as for those of the compensated voltage-control system (see Table on page 228 – items 1 to 5). The control-box checks are given in the Table that follows. Refer to the correct manual for the actual values to be applied to a particular unit.

Table 10.2 Checks for current–voltage system

Check	Result obtained	Conclusion	Remedy
6. *Voltage regulator* – voltage setting on open circuit. Disconnect B cable at control box. Connect voltmeter between D terminal and earth. Increase speed to 3000 rev/min.	Regulation occurs between 14·9 V and 15·5 V	Setting is satisfactory	
	Regulation occurs at other voltages	Setting not satisfactory	Adjust tension of spring blade and recheck
7. *Cut-out* – cutting in voltage. Connect voltmeter between D terminal and earth. Connect ammeter between B terminal and B cable. Increase generator speed. Headlamps on	Cutting in occurs between 12·7 V and 13·3 V	Cutting in voltage satisfactory	
	Cutting in occurs at other voltages	Cutting in voltage not satisfactory	Adjust tension of spring blade and recheck
8. *Charge current* Increase generator speed	Ammeter reading increases as speed is increased	Charge current satisfactory	
9. *Reverse current* Reduce engine speed	Ammeter reading falls to between 3 A and 5 A discharge and then returns to zero	Reverse current satisfactory	
10. *Current regulator* – generator must provide maximum output. Voltage regulator put out of action by use of spring clip to short out contacts to yoke. Ammeter between B terminal and B cable. Generator run at its charging speed	Ammeter reads between 19 A and 35 A according to type of generator	Setting is satisfactory	
	Ammeter reads more, or less	Setting not satisfactory	Adjust and recheck
	Readings fluctuate	Contacts dirty or air gaps incorrect	Clean contacts or readjust air gaps to correct settings

11

A. C. Generation and Auxiliaries

Rectifiers

The alternating current produced by a slip-ring generator cannot be used for battery charging until it has been converted into direct current (rectified). One method of rectification is by the use of a commutator as in the d.c. commutator generator. Another method is by the use of metal-plate rectifiers. These consist of a number of metal plates which are coated by certain chemicals and pressed very tightly together. In this form they have the ability to pass electrical current much more easily in one direction than in the opposite direction – in effect acting something like a non-return valve. These rectifiers are also known as semiconductors.

Selenium type (Figures 11.1 and 11.2)

In these an aluminium, or nickel-plated steel, disc is coated with selenium which is then heat treated to produce a crystalline structure.

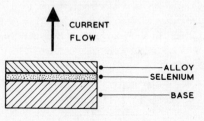

CURRENT
FLOW

ALLOY
SELENIUM
BASE

Fig. 11.1   Disc

The selenium is then coated by a low-melting-point alloy which ensures an even flow of current through the area of the disc. A number of such discs are arranged on an insulated central rod, together with spacers and much larger heat-dissipating discs or plates. The number and area of the discs can be varied to suit the current-carrying requirements. In this type current can pass easily through the discs from the steel or aluminium base to the alloy coating but only with great difficulty in the

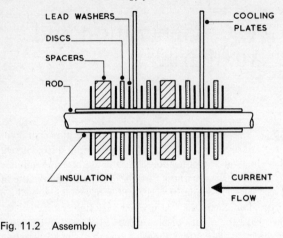

Fig. 11.2   Assembly

reverse direction. They may be arranged in series or parallel. It is most important that the temperature of these rectifiers should not exceed 55 °C or their characteristic property will be reduced or destroyed. Most are air cooled, but some of the larger units are oil cooled.

Diodes

These are very small but very efficient rectifiers made in the shape of buttons. They are used in alternators (a.c. generators) and are usually air cooled via a fan. In some large types they may be oil cooled and rectify currents of up to 215 A. In smaller alternators they may rectify currents of up to 65 A.

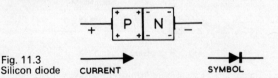

Fig. 11.3
Silicon diode

The diodes used in vehicle equipment are usually made from germanium or silicon (Fig. 11.3), the latter being preferred as it can be operated at higher temperatures without damage. The one-way current flow characteristic results from the flow of the carriers of electrical charge in each of the two parts, one part having free positive carriers (P type) and the other part having free negative carriers (N type).

Zener diode (Figure 11.4)

This is a special type of diode which will oppose the passage of current until a certain voltage is reached. When this 'breakdown' voltage is exceeded the current passes comparatively freely.

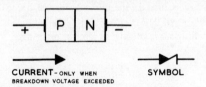

Fig. 11.4
Zener diode

CURRENT - ONLY WHEN
BREAKDOWN VOLTAGE EXCEEDED

SYMBOL

Transistor (Figure 11.5)

This consists of a three-part crystal of germanium, the parts being called the emitter, the base, and the collector. The emitter and the collector are made from germanium which includes a small quantity of indium and produces free positive carriers (P type germanium). The base is made of germanium which includes a small quantity of antimony and produces free negative carriers (N type germanium). In effect the transistor is a combination of two P-N type diodes, the base being between the emitter and the collector (P-N-P). Another type of transistor is the N-P-N in which the basic material is silicon instead of germanium. Silicon transistors can operate at higher temperatures than germanium types but both have to be cooled – usually by being arranged in air-cooled aluminium heat sinks.

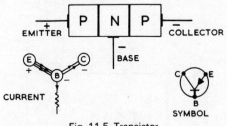

Fig. 11.5 Transistor

In a sense, the transistor acts as a current divider or splitter, and a relatively heavy current flow can be controlled by regulating the flow of a very small current. If the collector and base are made negative, and the emitter positive, current will flow from the emitter to the collector – via the base. If the base return circuit includes a resistor, a current entering the transistor at the emitter will be divided in such a way that a very small current passes through the base return circuit while the remainder passes through the base to the collector and its external circuit. If the base return circuit is broken the current flow to the collector is also broken or interrupted. These properties of the transistor are used in transistorized ignition circuits and in alternator control boxes.

A.C. GENERATION

Over the years the d.c. commutator generators have been made progressively smaller in size, lighter in weight, and greater in output.

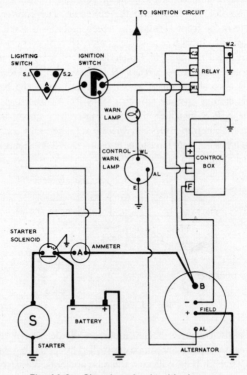

Fig. 11.6   Charging circuit with alternator

Without reverting to increased size and weight the limit has been reached with these generators – but the demand for more electrical power in vehicles increases every year. Increased traffic congestion also results in many vehicles having to operate for the greater part of their running time at very low road speeds, e.g. public service vehicles, taxis, ambulances, and police vehicles. Charging systems have therefore to produce larger currents at lower speeds.

The a.c. system, consisting of an alternator and its control system (Fig. 11.6), can easily meet these demands and has the following advantages over the d.c. generator system:

(1) A greater output per unit of weight.
(2) A greater output at lower speeds.
(3) A much higher possible operating speed.
(4) A simpler control system – the cut-out and current regulator not being required.
(5) A greater reliability – fewer and stronger rotating parts.

The disadvantages are those of greater cost and the fact that they must be designed as either positive or negative earth units, i.e. they cannot be interchanged between systems as a generator can.

NOTE. It is most important that the connections to the battery and to these units are *never reversed* nor allowed to short to each other or to earth. If this occurs the diodes and transistors will be destroyed immediately.

The alternator
The main parts of the alternator are the rotor assembly, the stator assembly, and the rectifier or diode assembly.

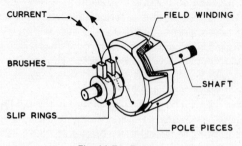

Fig. 11.7   Rotor

The rotor assembly (Figure 11.7)

This consists of a steel shaft which carries the driving pulley and cooling fan, a cylindrical iron core, and two insulated slip rings. A large number of turns of insulated wire are wound over the core to form the field winding. Each end of the winding is connected to its own slip ring and spring-loaded brush. The winding is enclosed by two iron polepieces with eight interlocking fingers which become alternate north and south poles when direct current is passed through the winding via the brushes.

The stator assembly (Figure 11.8)

This consists of a laminated, cylindrical, iron core which is slotted to permit the fitting of three sets of insulated windings. In the lighter units these windings are star connected and in the heavier units are

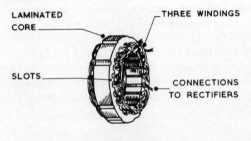

Fig. 11.8   Stator

delta connected. The stator assembly is fitted over, and very close to, the rotor assembly so the magnetic field of the rotor cuts across the stator windings as the rotor is forced to rotate. This results in the induction of a voltage in each winding, each voltage alternating in strength from zero to maximum. As there are three windings and three voltages the output is three-phase alternating current.

The rectifier assembly (Figure 11.9)

This consists of six diodes which are located in the end bracket of the aluminium-alloy slip ring. They are connected in a three-phase bridge circuit, three being connected to the bracket and three being insulated from it. Note that current can flow through the stator windings in

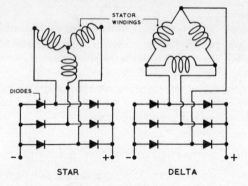

Fig. 11.9 Stator connections

either direction but it will be rectified by the diodes before leaving the alternator, i.e. the output is the total of the rectified currents. The bracket is used as a heat sink to assist in the cooling of the diodes, air being drawn through the alternator by the large-diameter fan at the pulley end.

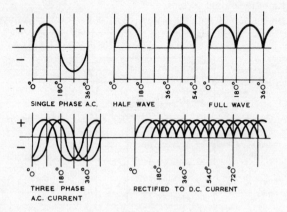

Fig. 11.10 Rectification

Operation

When battery current is passed through the rotor winding, via the control box, the winding becomes an electromagnet and produces alternate north and south poles at the pole fingers. As the rotor spins very close to the stator windings the magnetic fields cut across the windings and induce an alternating current in each one. Each current passes through its own diode and is rectified into direct current – the total current then being conducted to the battery.

THE A.C. CONTROL BOX

Two main types of control box are in service and in both the output of the alternator is controlled by varying the strength of the current passing through the field (rotor) winding. In the earlier types, control is obtained through the use of a vibrating-contact type of voltage regulator similar to those already described. In the later types, the current flow through the field winding is interrupted by the action of a transistor.

A current regulator is not required because the output of an alternator is limited by the reactance (inductive resistance) of the stator windings. Reactance increases automatically with the increase in the frequency of alternation of the induced currents and, as the voltage is limited by the voltage regulator, increased reactance automatically reduces the strength of the output current.

A cut-out is not required either, because the rectifiers (diodes) in the stator winding circuits of the alternator itself prevent the reverse

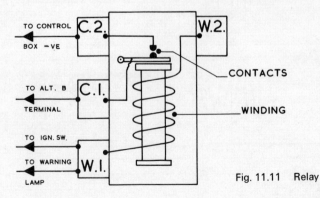

Fig. 11.11   Relay

flow of battery current. In many a.c. control systems, however, a field relay switch (Fig. 11.11) is incorporated for extra protection. This may operate to switch on a warning lamp when the alternator is not charging the battery, or to isolate the field winding and regulator from the battery when the alternator is not rotating.

Transistorized regulator (Figure 11.12)

This type of control box includes a vibrating-contact voltage regulator, a frequency coil, a discharge diode; a transistor, and a resistor. These units are arranged as shown in the circuit diagram.

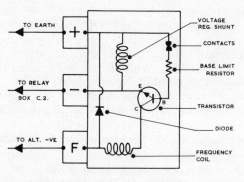

Fig. 11.12   Transistor regulator

Operation

When the ignition is switched on, battery voltage causes a current to flow through the emitter (E) and the base (B) of the transistor. The total current is then divided, a very small current (about 80 mA) passing to earth via the base resistor, the voltage regulator contacts, and the regulator yoke. The remainder of the current (about 2 A) passes through the base of the transistor to the collector (C). From the collector this current passes through the frequency coil to energize the field (rotor) winding.

When the engine is started, the alternator output voltage increases and, at a preset voltage, the contacts of the regulator are opened – so interrupting the flow of current to the emitter and the base of the transistor. This also results in the interruption of the flow of the heavier current between the emitter and the collector, and the field winding, and therefore in the reduction of the field strength and the output voltage.

As the output voltage falls, the regulator contacts are closed and the cycle is repeated. As the frequency of contact vibration increases with alternator output the maximum output voltage is not exceeded. The frequency winding is used to increase the speed of vibration, which provides a more steady output current. The discharge diode is used to protect the transistor from inductive current surge as the contacts of the regulator are opened.

Note particularly that the use of a transistor to interrupt the flow of the relatively heavy field current reduces the size of the current flowing across the contacts of the regulator. Arcing, and the burning of the contacts, is very greatly reduced and the contacts therefore have a much longer service life.

Warning lamp control (Figure 11.13)
The charging circuit includes a warning lamp, the light of which is extinguished when the alternator voltage is greater than the battery voltage. A simple lamp circuit connected directly to the ignition switch cannot be used because the lamp would be lighted by battery current flowing in one direction and alternator current flowing in the opposite direction, i.e. the lamp would not go out. A warning lamp control unit is therefore incorporated, the operation of which ensures that the light goes out when the output voltage of the alternator is greater than the terminal voltage of the battery.

In general arrangement the unit is similar to the flasher control unit

Fig. 11.13 Warning-lamp control

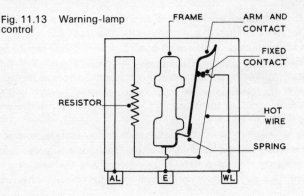

but the contacts are normally closed instead of being held apart. A fixed contact is connected to terminal WL of the control unit and the opposing contact is mounted at the upper end of a flat spring connected to the earth terminal E. The contacts tend to be opened by the spring but the upper end of the spring is held by a thin wire connected externally to the AL terminal of the alternator.

When the ignition is switched on the closed contacts allow battery current to flow through the warning lamp, the terminal WL, the closed contacts, and to earth – so causing the lamp to light.

When the output voltage of the alternator exceeds the battery voltage current flows to earth through the AL terminal, the resistance, the thin wire, and the spring. The passage of this current rapidly heats the wire which therefore expands – and the spring can now separate the contacts and cause the warning light to go out.

Electronic regulation (Figure 11.14)

Printed circuits are used in these control boxes, and the switching action, which controls the strength of the field current and therefore alternator out, is carried out by two silicon transistors. A Zener diode is used as a voltage control instead of a vibrating-contact type of regulator.

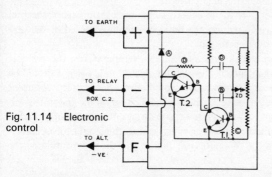

Fig. 11.14   Electronic control

When the ignition is switched on, battery current flows through a resistance to the collector of the first transistor T.1. and to the base of the second transistor T.2. At this stage the Zener diode prevents the flow of current in the base circuit of T.1. but normal transistor action takes place in the second transistor and current flows between its collector and emitter, i.e. battery voltage is applied to the field (rotor) winding of the alternator.

As the alternator is driven, a proportion of the voltage induced in the stator windings is applied to the Zener diode. At about 10 V this diode becomes a conductor and current flows through it and the base circuit of the first transistor. Current then flows between the collector and emitter of this transistor and so reduces the flow of current in the base circuit of the second transistor. This action in turn reduces the flow of current through the field winding of the alternator and so reduces the output.

The reduction of alternator output reduces the base current in the first transistor and increases that in the second transistor – increasing the field current again until the control action is repeated. The field current is therefore continuously varied to maintain the output voltage of the alternator at its preset value.

Detail (Figure 11.14)

The foregoing description is very much simplified and in practice the operation is greatly improved by the incorporation of the following:

(A) A diode across the field winding which protects the second transistor from the heating effects of the high voltages induced by the rapid collapse of the field current.

(B) A condenser across the collector and base terminals of the first transistor which reduces the radio interference caused by the very rapid switching operations.

(C) A resistance which prevents, at high temperatures, the possible flow of a small current through the Zener diode when it should be non-conducting. This current would affect the accuracy of output regulation by passing through the base circuit of the first transistor.

(D) A positive feed-back circuit consisting of a resistance and a capacitor, the operation of which causes the circuit to oscillate – so reducing the dissipation of power and the overheating of the transistors.

A.C. SYSTEM CHECKS

The following checks should be made, in sequence, in order to locate faults in the a.c. charging system. (Refer to manufacturers' instructions for details of settings, etc. related to particular units.)

(1) Check battery for state of charge (hydrometer) and for condition (high-rate discharge tester), as in all electrical checking.

(2) Check drive-belt tension.

(3) Check relay for correct operation. Connect ammeter between B- of alternator and B- cable end. Connect terminals C.1. and C.2. of the relay. Switch ignition on and run engine at about 1500 rev/min. If bridging the relay terminals results in the ammeter now indicating a charging current, then either the relay or its cables or connections are at fault. If a charging current is still not indicated the fault must lie with the control box or the alternator and their connections.

(4) Check control box. This is done by shorting it out, i.e. removing the F and −ve cables from the box and connecting them together. An ammeter discharge reading of 2 A to 3·5 A (dependent upon type) indicates that the field circuit of the alternator is satisfactory. When the engine is run at about 1500 rev/min the ammeter should indicate between 25 A and 40 A – depending upon the type of alternator. Lower readings than those specified for the type may be due to poor connections or cables, poor earth connection, or a faulty alternator. If this check results in accurate indications from the ammeter although these were not obtained before, then either the control box or its earth connection is faulty.

(5) Check voltage regulator.

(a) Vibrating-contact type. Disconnect heaviest battery lead from alternator output terminal and connect voltmeter with black cable to terminal and red cable to a good earth. Run engine at 1500 rev/min. The voltmeter should indicate 14·4 V to 14·8 V. If necessary adjust tension of spring blade. If adjustment will not bring the voltage within these limits the control box must be replaced.

(b) Electronic type. Check that battery is at least half charged. Connect the voltmeter across the control box (black cable to −ve and red cable to +ve terminals). Switch on ignition and run engine at charging speed. Switch on side and tail lamps, when the voltmeter should indicate 14·5 V to 19·9 V.

(6) Check alternator output. Connect ammeter into battery lead (battery must be less than fully charged). Switch on the full electrical load. Start engine and run up to 3000 rev/min, when the ammeter should indicate a charging current.

(7) Check warning lamp. If the various units and their connections have checked out satisfactorily but the warning lamp remains lit,

then either the warning lamp control unit or its connections are at fault. Failure of the lamp to light is usually the fault of the bulb but it may also be a fault in the control unit.

TRANSISTORIZED IGNITION SYSTEMS (Figure 11.15)

The main disadvantage of the conventional ignition system is that the output voltage of the coil is reduced as the speed of the engine is increased. Another disadvantage is that the erosion of the contact-breaker points, and of the sparking-plug electrodes, occurs fairly rapidly and affects the efficiency of the system.

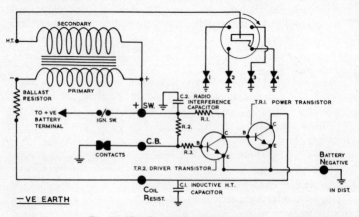

Fig. 11.15   Transistor-assisted ignition

These disadvantages may be overcome or reduced by the use of transistors. In one system the contact breaker is used only to interrupt the flow of a very small current through the emitter and base circuit of a transistor. The emitter and collector of the transistor are connected into the primary circuit so the normal action of the transistor results in the interruption of the heavier primary current without this heavier current passing through the contacts. The contacts therefore have a much longer service life. In these systems a much more rapid establishment and collapse of the primary magnetic field is obtained by the use of a low-inductance primary winding. This results in the production of much higher secondary voltages which are not reduced by an increase in engine speed, and a longer life for the sparking plugs as their normal erosion has less effect upon the higher-voltage sparks.

In another transistorized system the contact breaker is replaced by a rotating magnet device, the magnet producing electrical impulses which trigger an amplifier. The amplifier in turn actuates a spark generator connected to a distributor to supply the high voltages to the sparking plugs in the correct firing sequences. Once again engine speed is not a limiting factor in the efficiency of the system.

Disadvantages
These are that:
(a) The transistors can be permanently damaged by excessive heat.
  (b) The transistors will be destroyed if the battery connections are accidentally reversed.
(c) Where contacts are retained, oil or dirt can prevent the passage between them of the very small currents used in the base circuit of the transistor.

AUXILIARIES

Wiper mechanism (Figures 11.16 and 11.17)
The windscreen wiper mechanism consists of a small electric motor, a link or a flexible rack transmission, and the two wiper arm and blade assemblies.

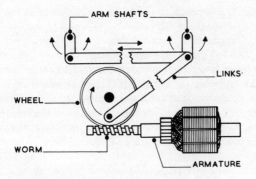

Fig. 11.16   Link type of wiper mechanism

The motor is of the two-pole, permanent-magnet type and has a high torque output to meet the demands of the articulated blades used on curved windscreens. The motor incorporates an automatic parking device which operates when the wiper is switched off, and it may also have a thermostatic switch which protects the windings in the event of an overload. This may occur due to packed snow, or ice, on the screen. Two-speed motors, which have three brushes instead of two, are available for high-speed vehicles. The usual speed of operation is about 100 wipes per minute.

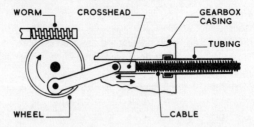

Fig. 11.17   Flexible rack type of wiper mechanism

The armature shaft has an integral steel worm which meshes with a nylon wheel. The wheel carries an eccentrically arranged pin on its upper face which is engaged with the end of the flexible rack. The angle of wipe can be varied by fitting a wheel in which the pin is located in a different position. The flexible rack consists of a cable which is overwound by a steel wire to form a rack, the rack being meshed with small wheels at the end of each arm shaft. The rack is enclosed by a steel tube and is lubricated by a special grease. The link mechanism is more efficient, but it has the disadvantages of requiring more space, due to the cranks at the ends of the arm and worm shafts, and of limiting the angle of wipe. In both cases the mechanism is given an oscillating motion by the action of the crank at the wiper gearbox end. The arms may be secured to their shafts by spring clips or split taper sleeves. The blades are secured to the arms by spring indentations. The 12 V type, under wet screen conditions, absorbs about 1·5 A.

Screen washer (Figures 11.18 and 11.19)
These may be manually or electrically operated. The manual types

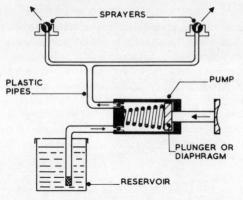

Fig. 11.18   Manual type of screen washer

consist of a reservoir, a simple plunger pump with two valves, one or two sprayers, and connecting plastic pipes. A filter is usually arranged at the pick-up pipe in the reservoir, and the direction of the sprays may be adjustable.

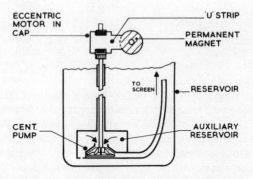

Fig. 11.19   Electric type of screen washer

In the electrically powered types the motor is built into the cap of the reservoir and drives the impeller of a simple, centrifugal pump immersed in the water. The motor is of the permanent-magnet type, a single magnet being arranged at one side of the armature and the field being completed by a U-shaped strip of metal which surrounds the armature.

Horns

Horns may be of the high-frequency, or of the wind-tone, type. Most British cars have matched pairs of the wind-tone type which produce a directed and penetrating sound which is not too unpleasant to the ear. The high-frequency horns emit a very powerful and piercing note and are usually fitted to motor cycles and commercial vehicles.

High frequency. In all horns the sound is produced by the vibration of a column of air, the vibration being caused by the rapid movement or oscillation of a diaphragm. The pitch and frequency of the sound is determined by the speed or vibration of the diaphragm. The loudness is determined by the extent of movement of the diaphragm.

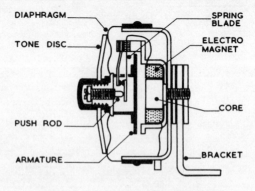

Fig. 11.20   High-frequency electric horn

The basic principle of the electric horn is that of a flexible steel diaphragm being attracted to an electromagnet, the diaphragm being distorted during the attraction and springing away from the magnet when the flow of current is stopped (see Fig. 11.20). The current passes through a pair of contacts, one of which is fixed while the other is mounted on a spring blade. When the diaphragm reaches the end of its movement towards the magnet a push rod attached to it moves the spring blade and so separates the contacts. This interrupts the flow of current, stops the action of the magnet, and allows the diaphragm to spring back away from the magnet. As this happens the contacts meet again and the magnet is re-energized to attract the diaphragm again and continue the sequence of operations.

The mechanism is enclosed by a case secured to a bracket which must be flexibly mounted and clear of obstructions. The diaphragm is mounted across the mouth of the case and carries an aluminium or steel tone disc. The later versions of these horns have either a low- or a high-frequency note, and they can be matched in pairs to give a very powerful warning note. These types have a condenser to protect the points from arcing during their operation.

Fig. 11.21   Single-horn circuit

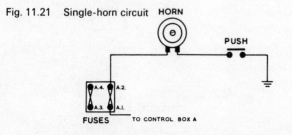

Where a single horn (Fig. 11.21) is fitted, it is usually supplied with current from the A.2. terminal of the control box or fuse block. The horn circuit should be protected by a 35-A fuse. Where a pair of these horns is fitted, volt drop in the cables could affect their operation. It is recommended that a separate circuit be supplied from the starter solenoid switch, and that it include its own 35-A fuse.

Adjustment, to compensate for contact wear, is required only after a very long period of service. An ammeter must always be used, and the adjustment varied until a specified amperage is obtained. In the earlier 12-V types this should be 2 A. In the later types, which have a fine adjustment screw, the amperage is between 2·5 A and 4 A at 12 V.

Wind tone. These horns operate on the same electrical principles as the high-frequency types but the diaphragm is arranged at the inner end of a trumpet. This consists of two die-cast halves which are bolted together, the mechanism being mounted on the upper face of the upper half. The sound waves produced by the rapid oscillation of the diaphragm travel down the trumpet, the length of which is such that the column of air vibrates at the same frequency as the diaphragm. This determines the pitch of the note while the shape of the trumpet determines the overtones. The trumpet is coiled to enable the length to be obtained without the excessive use of space. The diaphragm is so mounted that its edges are held while the centre is attracted by the electromagnet. The contacts are protected by a pellet-type resistance, these horns requiring a heavier current than the high-frequency types. The horns are usually fitted in matched pairs (Fig. 11.22) and are operated by a relay switch. This is to avoid the effects of volt drop in the circuit, the heavy currents being carried by heavier and shorter

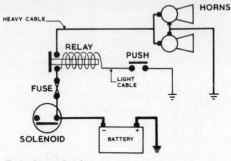

Fig. 11.22   Twin-horn circuit

cables and the relay being operated by smaller current and lighter cables. This is important where the cable has to pass up the steering column – space being very restricted. The current supply should be taken from the starter solenoid to the relay via a 50-A fuse. Twin wind-tone horns operating at 12 V usually require 13 A for their operation, while twin 6-V types require about 26 A. The adjusting amperage for these types of horn operating at 12 V is between 6 A and 8 A according to model.

Wind horns. A number of Continental horns incorporate an electrically driven air pump or compressor which forces air through two or more plastic trumpets in sequence. The length of the trumpets differ and so provide different notes. These types are also operated via relays.

Direction indicators

The older semaphore types of direction indicator have been replaced by the flashing-lamp type. In these a pair of lamps is arranged at the front and rear of the vehicle, the front lamps showing an amber or a white light when operated and the rear lamps an amber or a red light. The bulbs must have 21-W filaments and the lights must flash between 60 and 120 times per minute. A warning lamp must be visible to the driver and this is often built into the switch lever. One or more lamps may be fitted on the instrument panel.

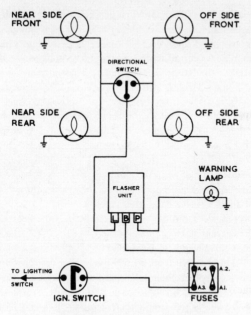

Fig. 11.23   Flasher circuit

The heart of the system is the flasher unit (Figs. 11.23 and 11.24). This is a thermal switch and it is hermetically sealed to prevent it suffering damage by damp or dirt. It must be mounted vertically with

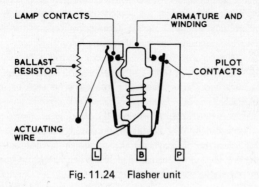

Fig. 11.24   Flasher unit

the terminals to the bottom, and in a position where heat and vibration are at a minimum.

The mechanism is mounted on a circular base plate which carries three terminals. A central steel core carries a winding, one end of which is connected to the lamps via terminal L. The other end is connected to a fixed contact which is also connected to a ballast resistor, i.e. the winding is in series with the resistor. An opposing contact is carried at the upper end of a metal strip secured to a spring at the foot of the core, and connected to terminal B. These contacts are normally held apart by the tension of the actuating wire arranged between the top of the strip and the ballast resistor.

When the directional switch is operated, the contacts being separated, current flows through terminal B and the metal strip, the actuating wire and the ballast resistor, and the series winding – passing through terminal L and the lamp filaments at one side of the vehicle to earth. Due to the current passing through the ballast resistor, the voltage at the lamps is insufficient to cause them to light but the filaments are preheated. This enables them to flash at the regulation 60–120 times per minute and protects them from the sudden surges of current.

The flow of current through the actuating wire causes the wire to heat up and expand. Its length therefore increases and its tension is reduced. This enables the top of the strip to move and the contacts to join. The strip is so shaped that its centre buckles or clicks as the top moves, the centre moving very quickly in the opposite direction. This simple mechanism acts in the same manner as the toggle mechanism in the electrical fuel pump – ensuring a very rapid make and break of the contacts, and being the source of the clicking noise heard as the unit operates. When the contacts are joined the ballast resistor is excluded from the circuit, together with the actuating wire, and the strength of the current is increased such that the lamps are now lit.

As the actuating wire cools it contracts, and its increasing tension pulls the metal strip away from the fixed contact. The buckling or toggle action occurs and the contacts are quickly separated to restart the operating cycle.

When the current flowing through the winding is strong enough to light the lamps (36–40 W being taken) the core is magnetized sufficiently to attract the armature carrying the moving pilot contact. As these contacts join, the pilot lamp is also lit. When the lamp contacts are separated the reduced current reduces the magnetic strength of the core, and the pilot contacts are separated by their armature spring. The pilot lamp therefore goes out of action at the same moment as the indicator lamps, and the correct operation of the pilot lamp shows that the indicator lamps are working properly.

Table 11.1   Faults

Symptom	Fault	Causes
No light at pilot lamp Click rate increased	One lamp not working	Filament broken Open circuit between filament and switch No earth connection
No light at pilot lamp No clicking	Two lamps not working	Open circuit between switch and first connector Both filaments broken
No light at pilot lamp No clicking	No lamps working	Open circuit between ignition switch and fuse A.3 Fuse blown Open circuit between fuse A.4 and flasher B terminals Flasher unit defective

Fuel gauges

These consist of a quantity-indicating gauge mounted on the instrument panel, and a transmitting or tank unit. The tank unit is a coiled resistance, varying lengths of which are brought into the circuit by the action of a float-controlled fork or bridge. When the tank is full the whole resistance is in circuit. When the tank is empty the resistance is excluded from the circuit.

In one type of gauge (Fig. 11.25) two small electromagnets are arranged to attract a small iron armature to which the indicating needle is attached. The flow of current, and therefore the strength of field, of one magnet is constant. The flow of current, and the strength of field, of the other magnet depends upon the value of the resistance included in the circuit by the action of the float. The armature and the needle therefore take up a position of balance and indicate the quantity of fuel in the tank. As the same basic voltage is applied to each magnetic winding the gauge is automatically compensated and the accuracy of the indication is not affected by the state of charge of the battery.

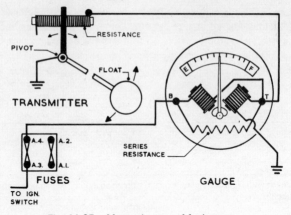

Fig. 11.25   Magnetic type of fuel gauge

In another type of instrument (Fig. 11.26) a bimetallic strip is heated by the current flowing through a heating coil wound over it. The deflection of the strip due to the heating effect is magnified and transmitted to the gauge needle. When the tank is full, the resistance is zero and the maximum current flows through the heating coil. Maximum

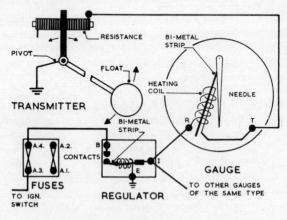

Fig. 11.26   Bimetallic type of fuel gauge

deflection of the strip occurs and the needle indicates full. When the tank is empty, the resistance is at maximum and minimum current flows through the heating coil. The deflection of the bimetallic strip is nil and the needle indicates empty. The accuracy of this type is affected by variations in the battery voltage and it is usual for all the instruments of this type on a vehicle to be supplied from their own voltage regulator at about 10 V.

NOTE. Battery voltage must never be applied directly to any of the terminals of either type of instrument.

Table 11.2   Faults (magnetic type)

Fault	*Causes*
No movement of gauge needle when ignition switched on	Open circuit between (a) battery and gauge B terminal, (b) gauge and earth, or (c) gauge and tank unit
Gauge indicates 'empty' when tank is full	As above
Permanent 'empty' indication	Open circuit between gauge and earth Short to earth between gauge and tank
Permanent 'full' indication	Open circuit between gauge T terminal and tank unit Tank unit not earthed
Permanent reading between 'empty' and 'full'	Float arm or fork seized in tank unit
Fluctuating readings	Loose connections somewhere in the circuit

Table 11.3 Faults (bimetallic type)

Fault	Causes
No indication	Fuse blown – cables short circuited. Low voltage from regulator (10 V required between earth and I terminal) Open circuit between gauge R and T Open circuit between tank unit case and terminal Open circuit regulator, gauge, or tank unit earth connections
Inaccurate indication	Low voltage from regulator Faulty gauge Faulty tank unit Partial short circuit on cables
High gauge indication plus overheating	Excessive voltage from regulator Short circuit between gauge and tank
Fluctuating readings	Loose connections Intermittent short circuits in cables Faulty regulator, gauge, or tank unit

12 Garage Technology

RECEPTION

The techniques of garage operation are the subject of many books and articles, and of much controversy. Only one or two points of interest can be touched upon here.

It is not sufficiently appreciated that the main purpose of *everyone* associated with a Service Station is to *sell* the various goods and services which the station can provide.†

Craftsmen in particular are usually very interested in their work and are proud of their skills – and this is as it should be. It is however all too easy for them to forget, or ignore, the fact that the main purpose of their work is to earn money for the station – so ensuring their future employment. It is not suggested that customers should be subjected to an amateur form of high-pressure salesmanship every time they set foot on the premises, but most customers appreciate the chance of discussing their difficulties with a craftsman – and it is at this time that they are most open to suggestions for improvements which could bring in future work.

The same applies to forecourt attendants and parts assistants, all of whom can, by their attitude to the customer and their work, so influence the customer as to make him or her feel that his interests are well looked after and that his custom is valued by the station.

Customers are initially attracted to a station which is conveniently sited, and which appears clean, tidy, and well cared for. It must be easy to enter and leave, and the forecourt must give the impression that fuel and minor services will be carried out without delay. In all dealings with the station the convenience of the customer is of paramount importance. Staff of all types must be polite and cheerful, and always give the impression of being willing and helpful. The customer must be able to park easily and find his way about without difficulty, the reception area in particular being well indicated, together with the routes to the Parts

† This subject is dealt with more fully in *Marketing of Motor Vehicle Parts & Accesories* by J. E. C. Moorey, published by Edward Arnold (Publishers) Ltd., 1969.

and Accounts departments. He or she must be attended to immediately or, if this should not be possible, be shown to a comfortable waiting room – after being given apologies for the delay.

There may or may not be a reception office, but whoever is responsible for the first contact with the customer has the most important task of translating the customers' requirements into work requirements. This involves the ability to talk and co-operate with all classes and types of people, most of whom have very little or no knowledge of the workings of the vehicle. Attempts to explain what is wrong have to be understood on the spot, the correct diagnosis made, and the correction work involved explained to the customer in non-technical terms. The diagnosis may involve a test run on the vehicle, with more explanations, or the use of modern fault-analysis equipment such as the engine analyser or the rolling road dynamometer.

When the diagnosis has been made, and the customer hands over the vehicle, the receptionist will allocate the work to the respective department – probably in the form of a detailed and technically worded job card. When the job has been completed, and passed by the tester, this fact will be reported to the receptionist, who will arrange for the collection or delivery of the vehicle.

SPECIAL TOOLS

The design and construction of the modern vehicle is such that the use of special tools, instruments, and setting jigs is always increasing. These tools, etc. involve the investment of considerable sums of money, and they must always be well looked after and readily available for use. They must be stored in such a manner that they are not subject to mechanical damage or damp conditions, and they must be checked for completeness on issue and return – many of these items including a number of small accessories.

One method of storing these items is by the use of shadow boards, the shape of the item being painted on the board to which it is clipped or hung. When the item is issued, a card is hung on the board giving the name and department of the person to whom it has been issued. Another method is to make these items subject to the normal issuing procedure of the Parts Department, the requisition form acting first as an item location form and later as a receipt for the person returning the item.

These special tools, etc. must be used in the correct manner and treated carefully to avoid distortion and damage. Damage must be reported at once in order that repairs can be made, or replacements ordered, quickly to avoid the hold up of subsequent work.

VEHICLE INSPECTION

The inspection of vehicles, or of their units or systems, may be carried out by any competent and experienced motor engineer, although professional qualifications are also required if his subsequent report is to carry weight as evidence in a court of law. An inspection may be carried out in order to (a) meet the requirements of an insurance company, (b) settle a dispute or (c) check that the condition of a vehicle meets the requirements of the Ministry of Transport for its use on public roads.

In the case of the various M.O.T. tests the report must be made out on a standard form issued by the Ministry; the equipment to be used, the test procedure, and the report are also all subject to the rules of the Ministry. In other cases the form in which the report is presented will be determined by the person carrying out the inspection – the report varying with the purpose for which it is required.

Inspection reports should provide the following information:
(1) The purpose of the inspection, the date it was carried out, and the place where it was carried out.
(2) The name and address of the inspector or examiner, together with his official capacity and professional standing.
(3) The items inspected, the results of the inspection of each item, and a professional opinion of the condition, etc. of each item at the time of the inspection.
(4) A general summary of the impression given by the inspection of the items under consideration, i.e. of the vehicle as a whole, or of the unit, or of the work carried out.
(5) The signature of the examiner, and of any other witnesses to his examination or parts of it, and the date.

Inspections must be carried out in a logical sequence, the more important items being dealt with first and the report on the findings being roughed out at the completion of each stage. If, for example, a complete check of the steering system were required, the inspection should start at the steering wheel, pass to the steering gearbox and then in sequence to the track rods and arms, the kingpins and stub axles, the hubs and wheels, and be completed by an inspection of the tyres.

Where the report may be used as evidence in a legal dispute the actual opening up of units should be witnessed and certified by another person, not necessarily a motor engineer. The units may be dismantled by the examiner himself, or by a mechanic or other craftsman under his supervision. The component parts must be laid out in sequence, and dirt or other foreign matter such as metal particles be examined before the parts are washed and examined in closer detail. In certain circumstances it may be necessary, for the purposes of evidence, to retain certain parts in the condition in which they were found. After a full examination, copies of the report detailing the evidence found, and the opinions of the examiner, are given to the person or company requesting the inspection.

M.O.T. TESTING

The M.O.T. system of compulsory tests for motor vehicles used on public roads is intended to reduce the numbers of vehicles being operated in such a condition that they are a menace to public safety. The tests are carried out at officially recognized service stations, or official testing stations, or by inspectors appointed by local authorities. A Certificate of Roadworthiness (Test Certificate) is issued for each vehicle which successfully passes the test, and this is valid for one year. It is an offence to use a vehicle, on a public road, for which such a certificate is not in force.

The test is designed to ensure that the brakes, steering, tyres, and lighting equipment of the vehicle meet minimum requirements with regard to condition, operation, and correct adjustment. Provision is made in the regulations for the owner of the vehicle to have the right of appeal to the M.O.T. in case of dispute with an authorized examiner over the report on the condition of the vehicle.

Service stations must be equipped with test instruments and facilities which meet M.O.T. requirements in both quality and number, and the test must be carried out in the manner specified by the Ministry. Service stations are inspected at irregular intervals by the Ministry inspectors to ensure that standards are maintained at the correct level.

Procedure

The procedure to be followed is specified in the *Testers Manual*, and in other publications issued by the Ministry and the Motor Agents' Association where advice is given on particular points of doubt or difficulty. These should be consulted for up-to-date details but the following may be of general interest and guidance to apprentice mechanics. If each question can be answered by 'yes' the vehicle should be able to pass the test. 'No' answers indicate that work is required before submitting the vehicle to a testing station.

Pretest questions

(1) Is the condition of the vehicle sound enough for it to be tested properly and safely? (Chassis and body condition sound, springs and shackles sound and secure, dampers operating properly, seat mountings secure, tyres sound and at the correct pressure, and the load secure.)

(2) Is the vehicle clean enough for the test to be carried out properly? (Oil and dirt not covering cracks, etc.)

(3) Is there enough fuel, oil, and water to last the duration of the test?

Test questions

Brakes

(1) Are *all* parts of the brake system securely attached? (Bolts, clevis pins, levers, cables.)

(2) Are levers, rods, cables in good condition and moving freely without undue slackness?

(3) Are all hoses and cables free from rubbing contacts?

(4) Are all hoses, connections, and cylinders free from leaks?

(5) Are all wheels hubs free from signs of fluid leakage?

(6) Is the fluid system free from air, and are the pedal and shoe adjustments correct?

(7) Is the hand brake acting properly and has it the correct amount of free movement?

Steering

(1) Is overall play at the steering wheel within acceptable limits?

(2) Are the steering and relay gearboxes securely mounted?

(3) Are all the ball joints and swivel pins free from undue stiffness, slackness, and signs of excessive wear? (Check lock-to-lock movement.)

(4) Are hub bearings correctly adjusted, wheel nuts right, and tyres centralized on the wheels?

(5) Are the tyres free from rubbing contacts on the vehicle?

Lighting equipment

(1) Do the lighting regulations apply to the vehicle?

(2) Has the vehicle the correct number of lamps at front and rear?

(3) Are the lamps clean, efficient, and correctly positioned?

(4) Are the rear lamps and reflectors red in colour?

(5) Are the headlamps correctly aligned?

(6) Does the beam-dipping mechanism operate properly?

(7) Are auxiliary lamps correctly positioned and their beams correctly aligned?

Tyres

(1) Are the tyres free from cracks and splits?

(2) Have they sufficient depth of tread?

(3) Are they centrally mounted on the wheel?

(4) Are they inflated to the correct pressure?

(5) Are the same types of tyre fitted at each side of each axle? (Radial ply or cross ply but not one of each.)

(6) Is the tread wearing evenly?

(7) Is the tyre free from plugged repairs?

Appendix: Examination Hints

The Author hopes that this book will help students to round off their years of workshop experience and college study by a very satisfactory final examination result, and wishes them every success in their chosen career in the motor trade.

There is more to passing examinations than trying to cram everything into your head and hoping to bring it to light again in the examination room. The questions you choose to answer, and the manner in which you set down your answer, has a great influence on your success or failure. Contrary to the opinion of many students, examiners do not set out to make students fail their examinations – but they do insist on certain standards of work being reached. This is not too difficult provided students will make a moderate effort to learn the subject matter, and will take note of a few points of examination technique.

Always remember that the only person who can guarantee your failure is yourself! You must be prepared to do some work on your own, your time at the college is all too short for the amount of work involved in the courses.

Preparation

I think it best to do about half an hour of studying every evening for the six weeks prior to the examination. Little and often is much less tiring, and far more effective, than a last-minute panic.

(1) Practise making labelled sketches – allow yourself no more than ten minutes to produce a diagram which shows the main details and is in fair proportion. Use a rule and compasses but don't waste time in shading or colouring – this can be done at the end of the examination if there is any time left.

(2) Practise writing down formulae, and rearranging them to obtain the various factors.

(3) Practise writing down definitions from science and technology until you can remember them without difficulty – these will often give you a lead into the understanding of a question.

(4) Practise writing descriptions and operational sequences by having a diagram in front of you and writing down what happens as the unit operates.

(5) Study and practise all the approaches to a topic of a subject at the same time, e.g. if the clutch is being studied examine sketches and read descriptions of the various types – noting the detail of components. Read why different types are used and how they are operated. Read up the science involved – friction, pressure, force, levers, and materials, together with the relevant calculations.

Examination

You should be in the examination room well before the time stated, to allow yourself plenty of time to settle down, arrange your equipment, and complete the form attached to the front of your answer book.

The time spent over each answer is of vital importance. With one or two exceptions, which are always pointed out, the questions carry equal marks, and it is most important that you attempt to answer the full number of questions required.

(1) Read through all the questions very carefully. Don't assume that a question of few words is necessarily easier to answer than one with a lot of words – the long one is very often long because the examiner wants to be sure that you understand it properly. Read all the parts of a question as a whole – this will very often give you a guide to the exact meaning of the individual parts.

(2) Select those questions which you know you can answer well and in all parts. Complete these first, ignoring their sequence on the question paper.

Make sure that you show every bit of your working out where calculations are involved. You can still get most of the marks awarded for this section if the examiner can check *easily* where you have made a mistake.

(3) Now select more questions. You will probably be able to answer the greater part of these and, providing you have not misunderstood any question, the time spent on these two groups of questions should have earned you sufficient marks to ensure a good pass.

(4) Now select the last questions which can at least be partly answered. How well you answer these·will probably determine how well you pass, so make a special effort to make a good job of them. Complete these in the final half hour.

(5) *Never* leave an examination room before the end of the examination. If you have done all you can, read through your answers and check that you have actually put down what you meant to put down. Check your calculations for correct answers and the use of the correct units. Check your diagrams to see if the units could work in the manner you have said they do. Use crayons or shading to emphasize the different parts. Give them bold outlines. Keep improving your work until the very last moment – it is amazing how the odd marks here and there add up to make the difference which will give you a Distinction or a First Class Pass. Always aim high – if you slip then you will still pass.

(5) Check that your examination number is on all work that you hand in.

Answer planning

Read your selected question very carefully once or twice and make sure you understand what you have to do to answer it properly. An examiner works to a marking scheme in which marks are awarded for each section of each part of the question. Your chances of success are improved if your answer follows the same pattern.

Plan your answer completely *before* you start writing any part of it. Make up a brief heading for each section for which an answer is needed, and jot these down in the margin under the question number. These will of course vary with the question but might read – construction – sketch – operation paragraphs – faults and causes table – calculation. In this way you will only miss out parts of an answer because you cannot answer them – not because you have overlooked them.

Sketches. Draw sketches and other illustrations a reasonable size, about 5 in by 4 in (130 mm by 100 mm). If they are much smaller, detail cannot be seen and if they are much larger they take too long to produce; examiners dislike postage-stamp, and poster, artists. Give outlines a boldness, and shade or colour different parts if there is time at the end of the examination. Work from centrelines and always draw what is at the centre first. Print all labels and use a large dot if you cannot draw arrows neatly. Be particularly careful when drawing springs and electrical circuits. A spring cannot work unless both ends are secured, and current cannot flow through a circuit which is not complete – it cannot start and finish at a dot on the paper.

Calculations. Draw a wide margin on the *right* hand side of the page and use this for every bit of calculation, even the most simple parts. Write down any formula, and what the symbols means. State the units used for each symbol and keep track of them through your working. Do not work out sections until an answer is required, and always look for figures which will cancel to simplify the work. Make rough checks to avoid silly answers. Don't be afraid of drawing a quick and simple sketch if this helps to make the problem easier to understand.

Experiments. Draw a neat sketch of the apparatus, and keep looking at it as you describe the working method. Keep your descriptions brief but don't omit essentials. Remember that science implies method and sequence, and logical conclusions.

Index